Phili   s

Straightforward

Upper Intermediate **Workbook**

with answer key

Macmillan Education
Between Towns Road, Oxford OX4 3PP
A division of Macmillan Publishers Limited

Companies and representatives throughout the world

ISBN 978-0-230-42338-1 Workbook
ISBN 978-0-230-42337-4 Workbook plus Answer Key
ISBN 978-0-230-42335-0 Workbook plus Answer Key and Workbook Audio CD
ISBN 978-0-230-42336-7 Workbook and Workbook Audio CD

Text © Philip Kerr and Ceri Jones 2012
Design and illustration © Macmillan Publishers Limited 2012

This edition published 2012
First edition published 2007

Designed by eMC Design Ltd.
Illustrated by Rowan Barnes-Murphy, Fred Blunt, Tim Kahane, Joanna Kerr,
Julian Mosedale.
Macmillan Reader Illustrations © Macmillan Publishers Limited 1999, 2002, 2005.
Cover design by eMC Design Ltd.
Cover photograph by Corbis/G.Kalt (main); Alamy/Robert Harding Picture
Library, Alamy/Images & Stories; Corbis/L.E.Frank, Corbis/R.Tidman; Getty/
D.Chinnery.
Picture research by Susannah Jayes.

Authors' acknowledgements
The authors would like to thank Nicola Gardner for her sterling work as Content
Editor. They would also like to express their debt of gratitude to Louise Fonceca,
editor for the Upper Intermediate level, the designers at eMC Design Limited,
Susannah Jayes for picture research and James Richardson for the sound
recording, who all played vital roles in the development of this new edition.
Finally, they would like to thank Katy Wright and the late David Riley, the
driving forces behind the first edition of Straightforward.

The publishers would like to thank all the teachers from around the world who
provided invaluable comments, suggestions and feedback on the first edition.
The publishers would also like to thank the following people for their help and
contribution to the second edition:
Tatiana Baytimerova (Russia), Lenka Boehmová (Czech Republic), Dr. Manuel
Padilla Cruz (Spain), Svetlana Elchaninova (Russia), Jennifer Díaz Green
(Dublin), Elena Mokeeva (Romania), Lynn Thomson (freelance editor), Amany
Shawkey (Macmillan Egypt), Maria Teresa Rius Villaplana (Spain), Natalia
Vorobyeva (Russia).

The authors and publishers are grateful for permission to reprint the following
copyright material:
Pages 62-63: Material used from website www.amnesty.org.uk, approved by
Amnesty UK;
Page 68: Extract from www.arbourvale.slough.sch.uk, reprinted by permission of
Arbour Vale School;
Page 37: Information on 'Gender Pay Gap' reprinted with approval –
http://europa.eu, copyright © European Union, 1995-2011;
Page 51: The Unicorn in the Garden' taken from Fables for Our Time and Famous
Poems by James Thurber (Harper Colophon, 1940), copyright © James Thurber
1940, reprinted by permission of The Barbara Hogenson Agency Inc on behalf of
the James Thurber Estate;
Page 15 & 27: Extracts from The Guinness Book of Oddities edited by Geoff
Tibballs (Guinness Publishing Ltd, 1995), copyright © Geoff Tibballs 2005,
reprinted by permission of Geoff Tibballs;
Page 69: Extract from website www.richardhill.co.uk;
Page 12: Extract from www.historic-uk.com;
Pages 90–96: Material from 'L.A. Movie' by Philip Prowse. Copyright © Philip
Prowse, first published 1999 for Macmillan Readers, reprinted by permission of
the publisher.

The authors and publishers would like to thank the following for permission to
reproduce their photographs:
Amnesty International UK pp62, 63; Alamy/Arco Images GmbH p15(br), Alamy/
Peter Barrit p18, Alamy/Blend Images p48, Alamy/Gary Cook p67, Alamy/
David Cole p74, Alamy/B. Christopher p28, Alamy/Peter Fakler p15(bl), Alamy/
Horizon International Images Limited p10, Alamy/ICP p72(cl), Alamy/Stan
Kujawal p69, Alamy/LMR Media p15(tc), Alamy/Ian Miles – Flashpoint Pictures
p47, Alamy/My Childhood Memories p57(bcl), Alamy/Radius Images p5, Alamy/
Mark Richardson p39(tcm), Alamy/Robert Salthouse p80, Alamy/Patrick Steel
p57(bcmll); Brand X p75(bc); Cartoonstock/Aaron Bacall p43, Cartoonstock/
Mike Baldwin p26, Cartoonstock/Adey Bryant p11, Cartoonstock/Marty
Bucella p70, Cartoonstock/ Ronaldo Dias p25(tl), Cartoonstock/Noel Ford p61,
Cartoonstock/Fran p46, Cartoonstock/Gordon Gurvan p20,Cartoonstock/Hagen
p34(br), Cartoonstock/ Richard Jolley p19, Cartoonstock/Andres Soria p34(bcl),
Cartoonstock/Robert Thompson p4, p14(cr), Cartoonstock/Mike Turner p29(cr),
Cartoonstock/Bradford Veley p7, Cartoonstock/ Caroll Zahn p59; Corbis pp36,
37(br), Corbis/Andrew Brookes p22, Corbis/Guy Cali p72(cr), Corbis/Hulton-
Deutsch Collection p75(tr), Corbis/Kruesselmann p37(bmr), Corbis/Yuriko
Nakao/Reuters p13, Corbis/Jessica Peterson/Rubberball p21(bl), Corbis/Frank
Tapper p75(bl), Corbis/Mick Tsikas/Reuters p81; Courtesy of Cyberbullying
Research Center (www.cyberbullying.us) p23; Digitalstock p14(b); Getty Images/
Peter Dazeley p9(tr), Getty Images/India Today Group p30(bl), Getty Images/
Johnny Johnson p15(cm), Getty Images/John Kelly p25(cr), Getty Images/
Mel Stuart p9(br), Getty Images/Time Life Pictures pp21(tr), 24, Getty Images/
WireImage p45(tr), 45(bc); HarperCollins p30(cr); ImageSource p39(b); Magnum
Photos/Gerda Taro © International Center of Photography p33tr, Magnum
Photos/Robert Capa © International Center of Photography p33b; Photographer's
Direct/Denis Erofeyev Photography p57(bcr); Photolibrary pp29(bcl), 40; Rex
Features/c.BBC/Everett p83(cr), Rex Features/c.Columbia/Everett p53, Rex
Features/Everett Collection p82, Rex Features/NBCU Photobank p83(tl), Rex
Features/SNAP p71; Science Photo Library/Sheila Terry p27; Reproduced with
permission of John Wiley & Sons, Ltd: Positive Psychology For Dummies by
Averil Leimon and Gladeana McMahon. Copyright © 2009 John Wiley & Sons,
Ltd., Chichester, West Sussex, England p66.

These materials may contain links for third party websites. We have no control
over, and are not responsible for, the contents of such third party websites.
Please use care when accessing them.

Although we have tried to trace and contact copyright holders before publication,
in some cases this has not been possible. If contacted we will be pleased to
rectify any errors or omissions at the earliest opportunity.

Printed and bound in Thailand

2016 2015 2014 2013 2012
10 9 8 7 6 5 4 3 2 1

Contents

p4	1A–1D	Leisure interests; Verb forms review; Negatives & questions; Saying *No*; Time adverbials; *What* clauses; Expressions with *thing*
p8	1 Reading	*All you need to know about … Sudoku*
p10	2A–2D	Adjectives (character); Present habits; Verb idioms; Expressing opinions; Past habits; Strong reactions; *Be/get used to*; Collocations with *get*
p14	2 Reading	*Bird brains*
p16	3A–3D	Compound adjectives; Expressions with *look*; Defining & non-defining relative clauses; Participle clauses; Slang; Addition
p20	3 Reading	*How to be a … celebrity lookalike*
p22	4A–4D	Word building; Explaining reasons (*so that, in order to, in case, otherwise*); Present perfect & past simple; Word class; Present perfect simple & continuous
p26	4 Reading	*Flying lessons*
p28	5A–5D	Narrative tenses; Art; *-ever* words; Evaluating; Past perfect continuous; Phrasal verbs 1
p32	5 Reading	*Close up: Robert Capa*
p34	6A–6D	Real & unreal conditions; *I wish* & *If only*; Elections; Embarrassment; *Should have*; *-isms*; Asking for & giving clarification
p38	6 Reading	*MPs' expenses scandal*
p40	7A–7D	The environment; Futures review; Expressions with *make*; Future perfect & future continuous; Giving examples; Nouns & prepositions
p44	7 Reading	*Sarah Burton – Dressmaker to the stars*
p46	8A–8D	Symptoms; Health idioms; Modals of speculation; Modals (permission, obligation & prohibition); Changing the subject; Phrasal verbs with objects
p50	8 Reading	*The Unicorn in the Garden*
p52	9A–9D	Adjective order; Adjectives with prepositions; Adjectives & modifying adverbs; Crimes; Compound nouns (jobs); Contrast
p56	9 Reading	*Batman*
p58	10A–10D	Reflexive verbs; Reporting; Collocations with *give*; Job responsibilities; Reporting verbs & patterns; Job interviews
p62	10 Reading	*Amnesty*
p64	11A–11D	Geographical features; *The* & geographical names; Binomials; Vague language; Articles; Describing landscape; *So* & *such*
p68	11 Reading	*Making Slough Happy*
p70	12A–12D	Passives review; Idioms (money); Passive reporting structures; Phrasal verbs 2; Causative; Generalizing; US & UK English
p74	12 Reading	*The Pharaoh's Curse*

Writing

p78	1A	Applying for a job (1)	p79	1B	Applying for a job (2)
p80	2A	A composition (1)	p81	2B	A composition (2)
p82	3A	A review (1)	p83	3B	A review (2)
p84	4A	An email to a friend (1)	p85	4B	An email to a friend (2)
p86	5A	A story (1)	p87	5B	A story (2)
p88	6A	A report (1)	p89	6B	A report (2)

Writing for Upper Intermediate students p76
Useful language to improve your writing p77
Short story: *L.A. Movie* p90
Answer key pi

1A | Consuming passions

LEISURE INTERESTS

1 Complete the text with words from the box.

> aficionado   crazy   get   got   give
> into   keen   obsessed   passion   take

HOW TO ... have a hobby.
In 10 easy steps.

1 You want to do something in your spare time.

2 So you decide to (1) _____ up a hobby.

3 You'll probably be introduced to it by a friend who's already (2) _____ on it.

4 You (3) _____ it a try, and immediately (4) _____ a taste for it.

5 Next thing you know you've (5) _____ the bug and you're buying all the equipment.

6 Gradually your hobby turns into a (6) _____.

7 You read magazines and books about it, you can't talk about anything else and your friends accuse you of being (7) _____.

8 You're so (8) _____ it that you take time off work to dedicate to it.

9 Soon you've become a complete (9) _____, an expert in your field.

10 It's not just something you do in your spare time anymore. You're (10) _____ about it. It's a way of life.

www.CartoonStock.com

VERB FORMS REVIEW

2 Find and delete one unnecessary word in each of the sentences.

1 She's does a lot of sport in her spare time.
2 We've has been taking part in a lot of competitions lately.
3 The winners were be given generous cash prizes.
4 They're is coming with us to the ghost festival next weekend.
5 He had have competed in a number of international tournaments.
6 I've always was been interested in photography.
7 We did went mushrooming at the weekend.
8 A new paintballing course was being been built.

3 Match the statements 1–8 to responses from the box.

> Does he?   Have you?   Were they?   Did it?
> Had she?   Has she?   Was I?   Are you?

1 You were always playing chess with your dad when you were a kid.
2 Did you know that Joanna's just taken up Thai kickboxing?
3 Dave spends hours and hours in the garage playing with his model train set.
4 I've just been asked to take part in a half marathon.
5 Helen was really tired last night; she'd just come back from a long hike in the mountains.
6 Did you know that Mum and Dad were thinking about buying a mobile home last year?
7 Our cat won the best-behaved cat award in last week's show.
8 I'm taking a diving course at the local swimming pool next month.

🔘 DICTATION

4 🔘 **01** Write the sentences that you hear.

1 _____
_____.

2 _____
_____.

3 _____
_____?

4 _____
_____.

1B | Unusual pastimes

NEGATIVES & QUESTIONS

1 Make the sentences negative.

1 Scientists have been studying tornadoes for a long time.
2 They understand the formation of tornadoes.
3 Tornadoes always have a central column of water (a waterspout).
4 Standing under a bridge will protect you from a tornado.
5 Tornado Alley is a closely defined region of the US.
6 Tornadoes are often found in the US outside Tornado Alley.
7 I'm planning to join a storm-chasing tour soon.
8 Many people had heard of storm-chasing before the Hollywood movie, *Twister*.

2 Complete the dialogue, using either question or negative forms of the verbs in brackets.

A: Steve, you've got an unusual hobby. What exactly (1) _____ (*be*) it?

B: Well, it (2) _____ (*be*) so unusual, you know. There are millions of people out there who do it every day. We just (3) _____ (*hear*) about it that much.

A: So, how (4) _____ (*you / get*) started? (5) _____ (*you / do*) it as a child? I mean, who (6) _____ (*give*) you your first Lego® set?

B: I was 8 years old when I built my first personalized model. I mean, I (7) _____ (*follow*) any instructions or anything. I just made it up myself.

A: And what (8) _____ (*be*) it a model of? (9) _____ (*you / get*) any help to make it?

B: My dad didn't actually help me, but he did give me a lot of encouragement. It was a very ambitious model – a copy of a bridge over the river in our town. I (10) _____ (*know*) at the time, but my dad entered it for a competition. I (11) _____ (*find*) out about it till a few weeks later, when a letter came through the post telling me I'd won!

A: And that was just the beginning! What (12) _____ (*you / work*) on at the moment?

B: A ten-foot replica of the Eiffel Tower.

SAYING *NO*

3 Complete the responses with phrases from the box.

> Are you kidding   I'm afraid not   I wish I could
> Not especially   Not exactly   Not to my knowledge

1 **A:** Will you be able to make it to the party on Friday?

   B: _____. I've got to be in London for a meeting.

2 **A:** Has Jamie signed up for the *Star Trek®* convention yet?

   B: _____. Or at least he hadn't when I last looked.

3 **A:** Did you tell Jane about the problem with the car?

   B: _____? I wouldn't dare! I was leaving it to you to tell her!

4 **A:** Did you enjoy the outing?

   B: _____. I mean it was OK, but it isn't really my kind of thing.

5 **A:** So you made this yourself, did you?

   B: Well, no. _____. I mean I bought the parts and I just had to assemble it.

6 **A:** Are you going to the match on Saturday?

   B: _____! But I've got to go to my mother-in-law's for lunch. It's her birthday.

TRANSLATION

4 Translate the text into your language.

Have you ever found yourself saying, 'I'll do my best', 'I'll get back to you' or even 'Yes, of course', when what you really wanted to say was 'no'? 'No' is one of the shortest words in the English language, but it is also one of the most difficult to say. Remember, if you say it politely, with a smile, it's much easier in the long run than agreeing to something you really don't want to do.

_____

_____

_____

_____

_____

_____

_____

1c | Autograph hunters

TIME ADVERBIALS

1 Complete the text with words from the box.

> afterwards   begin   end   finally   first   while

To (1) _____ with, I didn't really take much notice of them, but after a (2) _____ I started to listen to their songs and liked them. Then a friend offered me a ticket to one of their concerts. At (3) _____, I didn't really want to go. The ticket was too expensive, but in the (4) _____, my friend persuaded me and (5) _____ I was hooked! I started going to all their concerts, and then after months of chasing them around I (6) _____ got their autographs!

2 Match each of the words 1–3 to two words or phrases from the text in exercise 1.

1 initially
2 eventually
3 subsequently

VOCABULARY FROM THE LESSON

3 Choose the best word to complete the sentences, a, b or c.

1 We were allowed to go _____ to meet the stars.

   a) background   b) backhand   c) backstage

2 I don't usually give autographs, but I'll make an _____ for you.

   a) elimination   b) exception   c) overreaction

3 I was watching the limousines draw up when I felt a tap on my _____.

   a) shoulder   b) waist   c) ankle

4 Huge crowds turned up for the movie _____ at Leicester Square in the hope of catching a glimpse of the stars.

   a) show   b) viewing   c) premiere

5 Can you please add your _____ at the bottom of each page of the contract?

   a) sign   b) signature   c) autograph

6 She really wasn't surprised when he refused point _____ to sell.

   a) completely   b) totally   c) blank

7 Why don't you call the shop to ask if they've got any in _____?

   a) display   b) stock   c) trade

8 Both autographs and signed photos sell at incredible prices. Especially the _____.

   a) later   b) last   c) latter

4 Complete the sentences 1–7 with the phrases a–g.

1 He's gone to the main square to swap ...
2 If you don't do something to liven up ...
3 People often dedicate ...
4 She set up ...
5 The government is hoping to trade ...
6 Unfortunately, I won't be able to attend ...
7 You really ought to display ...

- [ ] a a lot more with South American countries.
- [ ] b football stickers with other collectors.
- [ ] c next week's training day.
- [ ] d the company with the money she made from car boot sales.
- [ ] e their books to family and friends.
- [ ] f this party, I'm going.
- [ ] g your collection on the walls of your house.

TRANSLATION

5 Translate the text into your language.

Alex-Li Tandem sells autographs – a small blip in a huge worldwide network of desire. It is his business to hunt for names on paper, collect them, sell them and occasionally fake them, and all to give people what they want: a little piece of fame. But what does Alex want? Only the return o his father, the reinstatement of some kind of all-powerful benevolent God-type figure, something for his headache, three different girls and the rare autograph of forties movie actress, Kitty Alexander.

Summary of *The Autograph Man* by Zadie Smith

1D | Collectors

WHAT CLAUSES

1 Complete the sentences 1–6 with the phrases a–f.

1 What always happens is …
2 What he really believes is …
3 What I don't understand about him is …
4 What I like most about my job is …
5 What I really hate most of all is …
6 What I've always wanted to do is …

☐ a the hours: they're very flexible and I can even work from home at times.
☐ b his attitude to his family. He really doesn't seem to want to spend any time with them.
☐ c the two of them end up fighting and arguing over who is the best.
☐ d having to clean up afterwards. It's so boring!
☐ e find a way to make money with my hobby. That'd be really great!
☐ f that if you really want to do something, you'll find a way to do it.

2 Insert *is* in the sentences.

1 What you don't understand he's happy enough as he is.
2 What you need to do find something to occupy your time.
3 What Bob wants a bit of peace and quiet after a hard day at work.
4 What you could do arrange for both of you to go out with friends.
5 What your friends can do suggest some other activities outside the house.
6 What you really need to do stop worrying!

3 Rewrite the sentences using a *what* clause.

1 I was just telling Bob that he should take up a hobby.

_____.

2 He really needs to get out of the house sometimes.

_____.

3 I've suggested he should give fishing a try.

_____.

4 I mean, it's very relaxing and it would get him out in the fresh air.

_____.

5 Bob thinks it would be boring.

_____.

6 He'd prefer to stay at home and read a good book.

_____.

7 He says I'm obsessed with unnecessary hobbies.

_____.

EXPRESSIONS WITH *THING*

4 Complete the sentences with words from the box.

about	another	in	good	past	those

1 I started out buying a couple on holiday, and then one thing led to _____, and before I knew it, I had a houseful of them!

2 She'd always had a thing _____ pigs. I don't know why. She's even got a cushion in the shape of a pig.

3 He used to love collecting model trains, but that's a thing of the _____. He's into boats now.

4 They're forever starting new collections. I've no idea what the _____ thing is at the moment!

5 She's totally obsessed by her garden gnomes. It's a _____ thing they've got a big garden.

6 What he gets out of it is a total mystery to me. It's just one of _____ things.

www.CartoonStock.com

'Fred brings home one too many cute refrigerator magnets.'

💿 DICTATION

5 💿 **02** Write the dialogue that you hear.

A: _____.

B: _____.

A: _____.

B: _____.

1 | Reading

1 Read the article and match the paragraphs 1–6 to the headings a–f.

- [ ] a How it started
- [ ] b How to play
- [ ] c World championships
- [ ] d Sudoku on TV
- [ ] e The meaning of the word
- [ ] f The popularity of the game

2 Read the article again and decide if the sentences are true (T) or false (F). Correct the false sentences.

1 Anyone who wanted could take part in the championship games in Lucca. _____

2 Most of the best Sudoku players are men. _____

3 No special skills are required to do Sudoku puzzles. _____

4 Sudoku magazines are extremely popular in Japan. _____

5 Sudoku was invented in Switzerland. _____

6 The first country in the world where people got the Sudoku bug was Britain. _____

7 The game of Sudoku is not always called Sudoku. _____

3 The sentences a–f were cut from the end of each paragraph of the article. Match the sentences to the paragraphs 1–6.

- [ ] a According to the rules of the game, only games with one solution are permitted.

- [ ] b However, she practises for two hours a day and is a regular visitor to the top Sudoku websites.

- [ ] c Other names include 'Squared Away', 'Single Number' and 'Nine Numbers'.

- [ ] d The magazine is now hoping that its new game, Kakuro, will prove to be equally popular.

- [ ] e The puzzle was an overnight sensation and Sudoku had become a household word.

- [ ] f Unlike crosswords, anyone can do it.

4 Complete the sentences with one word.

1 If something (a business, for example) takes _____, it becomes successful or popular very fast.

2 If you pick _____ on something, you react to something that you have noticed.

3 If you fill something _____, you complete it by adding information.

4 If you get _____, you have a high enough score to pass.

5 If you work something _____, you solve a problem.

6 If you turn something _____ something else, you transform or change it.

7 If you slip _____, you make a mistake.

Find these phrasal verbs in the article to check your answers.

5 Which of the statements 1–4 is closest to what you think about Sudoku?

1 I'm a real Sudoku fan and love doing the puzzles.
2 Sudoku is quite fun, but I can't understand why people get so obsessed with it.
3 I might give Sudoku a try one of these days.
4 I've got better things to do with my time than play games like Sudoku.

🔊 READ & LISTEN

6 🔊 **03** Listen to Reading 1 *All you need to know about … Sudoku* on the CD and read the article again.

All you need to know about ...
Sudoku

1 Called 'the fastest growing puzzle in the world', Sudoku was virtually unheard of in Europe until a few years ago. The craze first took off in Japan over twenty years ago and the Japanese now buy
5 hundreds of thousands of Sudoku magazines every month. When a British newspaper began publishing the game in 2004, its sales rocketed. Other newspapers were quick to do the same. Reports on CBS and other TV news channels
10 picked up on the craze and suddenly Sudoku was everywhere. There are now Sudoku magazines, Sudoku books and games for mobile phones.

2 The rules of Sudoku are simple enough, but the puzzle itself can be fiendishly difficult to solve. The
15 board has nine rows of nine squares and it is divided into nine boxes of nine squares. The player is given a few numbers to start with (no more than 32) and then has to fill in the grid so that each row and each box contains the numbers one to
20 nine once only. The puzzle requires no mathematical skill – it is a test of pure logic and concentration.

3 The first Sudoku World Championship was held in Lucca, Italy over two days in March 2006 and was
25 won by Jana Tylova, a 31-year-old accountant from the Czech Republic. The participants, who came from 22 countries, had to get through preliminary qualifying competitions in their own countries before making the journey to Lucca. The
30 85 qualifiers began with straightforward Sudoku grids before attempting more difficult variations, with the fastest person to work out the solution winning the most points. Tylova, the only woman in the top eighteen competitors, was unable to
35 explain the secret of her success.

4 Sudoku was probably inspired by the work of the eighteenth century Swiss mathematician, Leonhard Euler, but the puzzle as we now know it was designed by
40 Howard Garns, an American architect and puzzle constructor. His game was included in a New York puzzle magazine, but it was a Japanese magazine, *Monthly Nikolist*, that changed some of the rules and turned Sudoku
45 into what it is today.

5 Sudoku is an abbreviation of a Japanese phrase that means 'the numbers must be single'. In Japan, the word Sudoku is the copyright of the publishing company, Nikoli, so the puzzle is sometimes
50 referred to by other names such as 'Number Place', which was its original name in America.

6 In 2005, the first Sudoku show on TV was broadcast by the Sky channel in the UK. Nine teams of nine players (including celebrities) took
55 part in the studio while viewers at home could also join an interactive competition. To publicize the show, Sky TV carved a huge Sudoku grid, almost 100 square metres, on a hill overlooking a motorway in the west of England. Unfortunately,
60 the designers of the giant puzzle slipped up, as there were over one thousand possible solutions.

2A | Wildlife

Adjectives (character)

1 Match words from the box to their definitions 1–8.

> aggressive   cold-blooded   cute   ferocious
> inquisitive   obedient   playful   tame

1 keen to learn about a lot of different things _____
2 attractive, usually small, and easy to like _____
3 doing what a person, law or rule says you must do _____
4 trained not to attack _____
5 quick to attack _____
6 violent and able to cause serious injury _____
7 deliberately cruel and showing no emotion _____
8 lively and full of fun _____

2 Complete the sentences with words from the box in exercise 1.

1 Although rats are relatively small, they can be very _____ and should be approached with caution.

2 Tigers, panthers and lions are _____, wild animals. They are not suited for domestic life and should never be kept as pets.

3 Man is the most _____ killer in the animal kingdom, sometimes even doing it for pleasure.

4 Small children are naturally _____ and parents need to be patient in answering the thousands of questions they are forever asking.

5 If a large dog is not _____ to its owner, then it is a potential danger.

6 Children are often attracted to animals that look _____ in pet shop windows.

7 The deer in the park have become so _____ they will approach people and even help themselves to their picnics.

8 Take care when walking behind a young horse: a _____ kick could actually cause a serious injury.

Present habits

3 One of the three options in italics is not correct. Find and delete the phrase which is **not** correct.

The saltwater crocodile is the world's largest living reptile. Males (1) *will often grow / often grow / are often growing* to over five metres, whilst females are usually smaller, measuring around three metres. They have a reputation for being man-eaters, and although they usually feed on fish and crustaceans, they (2) *will also attack / have been known to attack / are often attacking* larger animals, including people. They are a particular danger in Northern Australia where there are several attacks every year. The local authorities (3) *will forever issue / are forever issuing / keep issuing* warnings and safety guidelines, but people (4) *will constantly ignore / are constantly ignoring / keep ignoring* them, with dramatic consequences. Fishermen (5) *will often feed / often feed / are often feeding* fish scraps to the crocodiles and this has made them even more dangerous, as the crocodiles (6) *have come / are always coming / keep coming* back for more.

Translation

4 Translate the text into your language.

Nile crocodiles, although physically capable of killing humans, can be very gentle with their own babies. Newborn crocodiles are tiny, weighing no more than 100 grams. In order to protect them when they come out of their shells, their mothers will place them gently into a pocket inside their enormous mouths. Then they will carry the babies to the water where they will proudly show them to their fathers.

_____

_____

_____

_____

2B | Animal rights

VERB IDIOMS

1 Replace the verb idioms in italics with phrases from the box.

> accept   explaining   interrupting   make sense
> misunderstood   saying 'no' to

1 I wish you would stop *butting in on* the conversation! It's really annoying!
2 I'm sorry, no matter how many times you explain it to me, it just doesn't *add up*.
3 Have I completely *missed the point* or do you really mean you're happy to do it?
4 There seem to be one or two things here that need *clearing up* before we go any further.
5 Look, you're just going to have to *face* it. They're not going to give you the job and that's that.
6 I've put up with about as much as I can take, but I'm definitely *drawing the line at* that!

2 Choose the correct verb idiom to complete the sentences.

1 He wasn't found guilty of the crime, because all the evidence just didn't *clear up / add up*.
2 We're going to have to *face / clear up* the fact that we aren't wanted.
3 They had *missed the point / drawn the line* and were absolutely refusing to go any further.
4 It was obvious that he had totally *cleared it up / missed the point* and didn't know what was going on.
5 Just as I was coming to the best part of the story he *butted in / added up* and stopped me in mid-flow.
6 It took us ages to explain what had gone wrong, but in the end we managed to *draw the line / clear it up*.

EXPRESSING OPINIONS

3 Complete the opinions with words from the box.

> ask   concerned   convinced   don't
> honest   personally   think   wrong

A

1 I may be _____, but aren't humans more important than animals?
2 If you _____ me, keeping pets is a waste of time and money.
3 As far as I'm _____, dogs are dirty animals and shouldn't be allowed in public places.
4 I'm absolutely _____ that pets grow to look like their owners.

B

☐ a I really _____ think there's any need to be so extreme.

☐ b Frankly I _____ it's the other way round.

☐ c To be perfectly _____, no. We do far more harm than all other species put together.

☐ d _____, I think they have a role to play as companions for elderly people.

4 Look at the sentences in exercise 3 again. Match an opinion in A to a response in B.

🔘 DICTATION

5 🔘 **04** Write the text that you hear.

_____

_____

_____

_____

_____

'The foxes in this area seem to have adapted well to urban life.'

2c | Companions

Past habits

1 Rewrite the sentences with the words in brackets.

1 I remember that my grandmother had a beautiful garden. (*used to*)
2 She spent hours in her garden in summer, watering the plants and tending the flowers. (*would*)
3 She didn't like us playing near the flower beds. (*used to*)
4 So she built a special playground where we spent hours and hours every holiday. (*would*)
5 We loved that playground and I was really sorry when she moved into a smaller house. (*used to*)
6 She still had a garden, but it wasn't so big and on our weekly visits we played inside the house instead. (*would*)

2 Find and correct four mistakes in the verbs in italics.

Famous British Eccentrics # 18

Lord Rokeby decided that he would like to spend all his life near or in water. He (1) *would spend* hours in the sea off the Kent beaches, and his servants often (2) *used to have to* drag him out on to dry land, unconscious. As he got older, at his country home, he (3) *used to have* a vast tank built with a glass top, had it filled with water and (4) *used to spend* all day floating in the water. He once (5) *would grow* the most enormous beard. He (6) *would be* very proud of it. It (7) *used to hang down* to his waist and spread out on the surface of the water. He (8) *would take* his meals in his pool, to the embarrassment of his family. His obsession with water was so great that he (9) *would drink* great quantities every day. He (10) *used to live* to be 88, so he was a good advertisement for the health-giving properties of water!

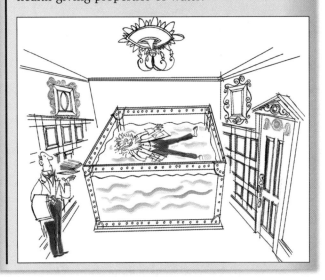

Strong reactions

3 Look at the dictionary definition and complete the examples.

> **mad** /mæd/ adj ＊＊
> **1** very silly or stupid: CRAZY **sb must be mad to do sthg** *mainly spoken* used for saying that someone is doing something very stupid.
> **2** [never before a noun] *informal* angry. **drive sb mad** *informal* to make someone feel extremely angry, upset or bored **go mad** *informal* **1** to become mentally ill **2** to become crazy because you are so bored, upset, etc
> **like mad 1** very quickly and with great effort
> **2** a lot
> **3** in a way that you cannot control or stop.
> **mad about/on sth** *informal* very enthusiastic about something

1 Dad _____ mad when he saw the mess.
2 He _____ me mad the way he keeps criticizing me all the time.
3 I would _____ mad if I had to live with him.
4 My kids are mad _____ computer games.
5 We had to work _____ mad to finish the job before the weekend.
6 You _____ be mad to sell that beautiful house.

4 Choose the best word to complete the sentences.

1 He's usually really even-tempered, but when he does get angry, he really *loses / blows* his top.
2 I don't usually get worked *up / out* about problems.
3 And whatever you do, please, please try not to *lose / blow* your temper.
4 You what? You paid £5,000 for that. You need your *head / top* examined!
5 When she saw what had happened to the window, she was absolutely *lunatic / livid*.
6 He's mad, totally and completely *round / on* the bend.
7 You'd have to be *totally / complete* insane to even consider doing that!

Dictation

5 🔘 **05** Write the dialogue that you hear.

A: _____.

B: _____?

A: _____.

B: _____?

A: _____.

2D | Working animals

BE/GET USED TO

1 Choose the correct verb form to complete the sentences.

1 I don't think I'll ever *be / get* used to the way he treats his dogs.
2 I was brought up on a farm, so *I'm / I'm getting* used to working with animals.
3 I've lived here for three years, but I still haven't *been / got* used to the heat.
4 We prefer it if volunteers *are / get* already used to working with the blind.
5 I hate having to get up so early, but my husband *is / gets* used to it and says he loves it.
6 It took me a long, long time to *be / get* used to my new way of life.

2 Complete the text with *are used to*, *get used to* or *used to*.

The makers of virtual pets claim that the toy helps children (1) _____ the responsibilities involved in looking after a real pet. I'm not so sure. My kids (2) _____ have one when they were smaller, but their interest in them disappeared pretty fast, and they soon got bored. Much the same thing (3) _____ happen with our real pets when I was a kid. But now a new virtual pet has appeared in the shops and we're going to try again. We haven't had it very long, but we (4) _____ having it around already. Its attention-seeking beep can be pretty annoying to start with. It (5) _____ wake us up in the middle of the night, although you soon (6) _____ it. The kids love it. The new version is much more responsive, much more fun than the one we (7) _____ have and I highly recommend it. It may not teach the kids to be more responsible, but it certainly keeps them happy on long car journeys. If your kids (8) _____ playing with other pocket-sized computer games, then they'll love the new virtual pocket pets. And if you (9) _____ not _____ them – watch out, these pets can be pretty addictive!

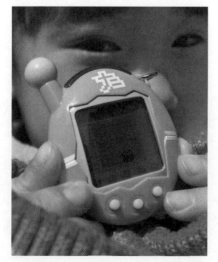

COLLOCATIONS WITH GET

3 Rewrite the sentences with the correct form of expressions from the box.

> get along   get around   get in touch with
> get involved with   get on with it

1 I first started doing voluntary work when I was at university.

   _____.

2 To start with, I didn't really have a very good relationship with our new neighbours.

   _____.

3 Stop wasting time and just do what you've got to do!

   _____!

4 Travelling by car in the centre of town can be quite stressful with all the traffic jams.

   _____.

5 I'll call you as soon as I hear any news.

   _____.

4 Rewrite the text by replacing the word *got* and making any other necessary changes.

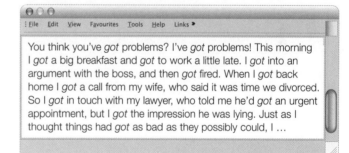

You think you've *got* problems? I've *got* problems! This morning I *got* a big breakfast and *got* to work a little late. I *got* into an argument with the boss, and then *got* fired. When I *got* back home I *got* a call from my wife, who said it was time we divorced. So I *got* in touch with my lawyer, who told me he'd *got* an urgent appointment, but I *got* the impression he was lying. Just as I thought things had *got* as bad as they possibly could, I …

5 Can you continue the story in exercise 4 with any more *get* expressions?

TRANSLATION

6 Translate the sentences into your language.

1 Things definitely aren't what they used to be.
2 You'd better get used to it, because it's not going to change.
3 As soon as we're used to doing one thing, we have to learn another.
4 That's one thing I'll never get used to doing.
5 We never used to, but we get on quite well now.
6 I've never really got used to being married and getting called 'Mrs'.

2 | Reading

1 Use a dictionary to find the odd word out in the box.

> beak   chick   compost   hatch
> incubate   lay (an egg)   nest   wing

2 Explain the words in italics in your own words.

1 His ideas were completely *bird-brained*.
2 I won't listen to your *bird-brained* ideas any longer.
3 Even a complete *bird brain* could answer that question.
4 Stop behaving like a *bird brain* and do something intelligent with your life.

3 Read the article. Which birds A–D:

1 build their nests near sand?
2 have to care for themselves as soon as they are born?
3 live together as a threesome?
4 lock themselves away for a few months?
5 place a stone at the female's feet?

4 Match the explanations a–e to the actions 1–5 in exercise 3.

- [ ] a because the males do not want to separate.
- [ ] b because they are abandoned by the parents.
- [ ] c in order to attract her.
- [ ] d in order to avoid dangerous animals.
- [ ] e so that they can use it to change the temperature of their eggs.

5 Find words in the article that match the definitions 1–5.

1 moves forward while turning over and over (bird A)
2 are born out of an egg (bird B)
3 covering something with a layer or pile of things (bird C)
4 not consider something or not let it influence you (bird C)
5 closes a container or space by covering it with something (bird D)

6 Explain the proverbs in your own words.

1 A bird in the hand is worth two in the bush.
2 Every bird loves to hear himself sing.
3 The early bird catches the worm.

⊙ READ & LISTEN

7 ⊙ **06** Listen to Reading 2 *Bird Brains* on the CD and read the article again.

www.CartoonStock.com

'I love a scary film.'

BIRD BRAINS

1 When the male **Adele penguin** (A) is looking for a mate, he takes his pick from a colony of more than a million. Having made his choice, he needs to impress the female bird he has selected. In order to do this, he finds a suitable stone, rolls it over to the female and hopes that she will accept his gift. If he's in luck, the two birds will stand next to each other, breast to breast, sing loudly and make a lot of noise with their flippers flapping. If the male fails to impress with his stone, he will have to be a bit less choosy next time. With so many other males also rolling stones around the place, he may also find that stones are in short supply. When that happens, the only thing to do is find a smaller male penguin and steal his stone.

2 **Geese** (B) and humans have at least one thing in common. They both have lasting relationships with their partners. Male geese sometimes prefer the company of other male geese, but this doesn't stop them from raising a family. The males can be joined by a female bird, and both males will look after the eggs she lays, and the tiny goslings that hatch.

3 Most birds use body heat to incubate their eggs, but the **Mallee fowl** (C), a member of the brush-turkey family from Australia and the Pacific Islands, keeps its eggs warm by burying them in a compost heap of rotting vegetation. As well as looking after the eggs, the male continually checks the temperature of the incubator with his beak. His aim is to ensure that the inside of the compost heap remains almost constantly at 33°C and he achieves this by adding or removing a layer of sand, when necessary. Ironically, after such care and devotion, as soon as the eggs are hatched, the parents totally ignore the chicks, which are forced to look after themselves immediately.

4 The home of the **Great Indian Hornbill** (D) is a prison. When the female is ready to lay her eggs, she hides in a hole in a tree. The male then seals up the hole, leaving just a narrow slit through which he passes food. Although she is unable to get out, the female has the consolation of knowing that the eggs are safe from predators such as snakes and monkeys. The female stays in there until the chicks are a few months old. She then helps the male with the feeding.

3A | Fashion statements

COMPOUND ADJECTIVES

1 Complete the missing parts of the compound adjectives.

He's (1) middle-a_____, but looks younger and is extremely (2) easy-g_____. Some days he's (3) clean-s_____ and other days he looks as if he's growing a beard. He wears comfortable, casual clothes. I think quite a few of them may be (4) second-h_____. He's particularly fond of his (5) worn-o_____ jeans, and although he's (6) well-o_____ and could afford to buy himself a whole new wardrobe, he really doesn't care.

2 Match a word from each box to form six compound adjectives.

anti	knee	middle	never	old	short

class	ending	establishment	fashioned
lived	length		

3 Complete the sentences with the compound adjectives in exercise 2.

1 Many teenage fashions claim to be rebellious and _____.

2 I remember when _____ skirts were considered incredibly boring, only to be worn as part of a school uniform.

3 Fashions in clothes and music just keep going round in _____ circles, constantly reworked and repeated.

4 Nothing is more _____ than this year's latest fashion fad. It'll have been completely forgotten in six months' time.

5 There's a thin line between being _____ and rediscovering a look from the recent past.

6 Designer fashion did not use to be for _____ women, but more people can afford it now.

VOCABULARY FROM THE LESSON

4 Complete the descriptions with words from the box.

ethnic flared make-up patterns provocative
ripped safety pins velvet wide-collared

TRIBAL UNIFORMS

The Ted

Long, knee-length (1) _____ jackets, straight waistcoats and (2) _____ shirts

The Hippy

(3) _____, Indian-inspired jewellery, (4) _____ denim jeans, loose tops with flowery or psychedelic (5) _____

The Punk

(6) _____, scruffy clothes, T-shirts with (7) _____ slogans and studs or (8) _____ as jewellery

The Goth

Black, nineteenth-century style clothes and dark (9) _____

TRANSLATION

5 Translate the text into your language.

Skateboarding has grown in popularity as an expression of youth culture over the last 30 years. Initially it was associated very closely with surfing culture, but nowadays skateboarding has its own stereotypes, music and fashions. The traditional skateboarding look is one of over-sized jeans and big, loose T-shirts, but recently skaters are tending more towards much tighter trousers and skin-tight T-shirts.

_____

_____

_____

3B | The right look

EXPRESSIONS WITH *LOOK*

1 Complete the sentences with words from the box.

best	exchanged	feminine	got
have	sophisticated	through	

1 Judging from the looks we _____, I think we might have been a bit overdressed.

2 She was looking her very _____, but it still wasn't good enough.

3 I looked _____ the catalogue over and over, but I still couldn't find anything suitable.

4 As he got up to speak, the two girls _____ looks and burst out laughing.

5 I'm trying to go for a _____ look, something stylish and classy.

6 Did you _____ a look at that new shirt I got for you? What did you think?

7 It's nice, but it's a bit _____-looking for a guy, though. Don't you think?

2 Complete the sentences 1–6 with the phrases a–f.

1 I could tell by the look on his face …
2 Even as she grew older, …
3 I took one look at him …
4 Brian looked as …
5 I was furious: he had made me look …
6 It's not a good idea to travel without insurance – look …

☐ a she never lost her looks.
☐ b if he was going to cry.
☐ c what happened to Bill!
☐ d that he wasn't happy.
☐ e a complete idiot!
☐ f and decided I didn't like him.

3 Match the examples of *look* in the sentences in exercise 2 to the uses.

> **look 1** /lʊk/ verb ★★★
> 1 direct your eyes towards someone or something/ used to draw somebody's attention _____
> 2 have an appearance/seem to be _____
> **look 2** /lʊk/ noun ★★★
> 1 act of looking at somebody _____
> 2 expression on face/in eyes _____
> 3 appearance/style _____

DEFINING & NON-DEFINING RELATIVE CLAUSES

4 Circle all the possible options for each sentence.

1 It's difficult to know what to wear when you're meeting someone *which / who / that* you've never met before.
2 The best thing to do is opt for something neutral, *which / who / that* is usually easy enough.
3 The most important thing is to choose something *which / who / that* you feel comfortable in.
4 You may want to wear something brand new *which / who / that* you've bought especially for the occasion.
5 It depends very much on the nature of the meeting and the person *which / who / that* you're going to meet.
6 Remember, what you say and what you do are far more important than the clothes *which / who / that* you choose to wear.

5 Decide which of the relative pronouns in italics can be omitted.

They invited us round for dinner, (1) *which* was nice. Sue cooked a special Greek dish (2) *that* she'd had on holiday. It was delicious, with fresh vine leaves (3) *that* she'd managed to buy at the local market. Her sister was there, too, the one (4) *who* has just come back from the States. She was looking very glamorous in a little black cocktail dress (5) *that* she'd picked up in New York. It was covered in tiny little sequins (6) *that* glowed in the candlelight. John couldn't take his eyes off her all night!

🔊 DICTATION

6 🔊 07 Write the sentences that you hear.

1 _____.

2 _____.

3 _____.

4 _____.

3c | Mirror images

PARTICIPLE CLAUSES

1 Rewrite the participle clauses in bold as full relative clauses.

Take a look at any portrait (1) **depicting a young woman** from any time in history and you will quickly understand the principles of beauty (2) **held to be universal** in that age. For example, take a look at Goya's reclining woman, 'Maya', whether (3) **dressed or undressed**, and you will understand that curves and a full figure, (4) **now considered unattractive,** were the standard of beauty at the time. Compare her to today's supermodels and underfed film stars, (5) **starving themselves to death** in order to conform to the 21st century's idea of female beauty. You don't even need to look back as far as the 19th century. Any photo of Marilyn Monroe or Sophia Loren, (6) **either posing for photographers or starring in the Hollywood blockbusters of the time**, show the same voluptuous concept of the ideal woman.

2 Rewrite the relative clauses in italics as participle clauses.

1 People *who live and work in modern cities* have no time to eat properly.
2 Young girls *who are growing up in today's consumer society* are bombarded by images of the 'perfect body'.
3 Actors or actresses *who are paid to represent beauty products* should be held responsible for the images they promote.
4 Even magazines *that claim to cover serious news stories* often feature images of celebrities.
5 Hollywood blockbusters, *which are seen by millions of cinema-goers all over the world*, invariably choose slim women in their star roles.
6 It is very difficult to control images *which are made available on the internet*.

VOCABULARY FROM THE LESSON

3 Complete the text with words from the box.

blemish	cloud	eating
set	spotlight	susceptible

Incomprehensible as it may be to their fans, the rich, famous and beautiful are just as (1) _____ to **self-doubt** as anyone else. No matter how **stunning** they are, the constant attention and media coverage often

(2) _____ their judgment. Every **pimple** and spot is seen as a major (3) _____ and any departure from the media-dictated norms of beauty is seen as **abnormal**. Many stars have been in the (4) _____ since **puberty**, whether on a Hollywood film (5) _____ or on the front pages of gossip magazines. So it comes as no surprise to hear that many of these celebrities suffer from serious (6) _____ disorders.

4 Complete the dictionary extracts with the words in bold in exercise 3.

1 _____ *adj* ★ not usual or typical, especially in a way that is worrying or shows that there may be something wrong or harmful

2 _____ *adj* impossible to understand

3 _____ *noun* [C] a small red lump on your skin, especially your face

4 _____ *noun* [U] the period in adult life when a child changes physically into an adult

5 _____ *noun* [U] the feeling of not having confidence in your abilities

6 _____ *adj* ★ extremely attractive

⊙ DICTATION

5 ⊙ 08 Write the text that you hear.

_____

_____

_____

_____

_____

_____

_____

Naomi Wolf

3D | Model behaviour

Slang

1 Match words from the box to their definitions 1–8.

> an airhead   beat   blow   a drag
> dumb   a grand   nuts   psyched up

1 crazy _____

2 stupid _____

3 very tired _____

4 something or someone that is boring or causes small annoying problems _____

5 a thousand pounds or dollars _____

6 extremely excited or nervous _____

7 a silly or stupid person _____

8 to spend a lot of money quickly on things that you do not need _____

'What's that funny look for? You think my girlfriend's an airhead, don't you?'

2 Complete the sentences with words in exercise 1.

1 We'd been working all night and I was _____!

2 Yeah, can you believe it, he's won the lottery and he's going to _____ it all on a car!

3 So are you all _____ for the competition this afternoon?

4 I hate filling in all these forms; it's such _____.

5 She's just so dizzy and distracted – a complete _____.

6 I can't believe you just did that. I mean, it's just so _____!

7 He's just totally _____ about her – completely head over heels in love.

8 Yeah, it was pretty expensive – cost us more than ten _____ in the end.

Addition

3 Put the lines in the correct order.

☐ all of that – you get paid loads and loads of money! What could be better?

☐ you also get to stay in superb five-star hotels where the welcome is just great! What's

☐ as working with some of the world's most famous photographers. And on top of

☒ I absolutely love it. I mean, besides

☐ more, you get to meet all these really interesting people as well

☐ getting the chance to travel to all these fantastic places,

Translation

4 Translate the extract from a magazine index into your language.

78 SUMMER ACCESSORIES
you can't afford to be without

♥ **HEALTH AND BEAUTY** 🍸

83 PREGNANCY –
the importance of staying proud of your body

87 CHOOSING A PLASTIC SURGEON –
ten questions you should ask before going any further

94 HOW TO FIND THE RIGHT BODY SIZE FOR YOU –
and feel good about it!

96 NEW BEAUTY PRODUCTS –
we've tested all the latest from the high street shelves

97 GET A TAN –
take advantage of our special offer and get 10% off a range of sunbeds and super winter tan creams.

3 | Reading

1 Look at the dictionary entry. How do you say *lookalike* in your language?

> **lookalike** /ˈlʊkəlaɪk/ noun [C] someone who is very similar in appearance to another person, especially a famous person: *a Tom Cruise lookalike*

2 Read the interview with a celebrity lookalike and match the questions a–e to the answers.

- ☐ a Have you got any plans for a change of career?
- ☐ b How long have you been doing it?
- ☐ c Are all lookalikes professional actors?
- ☐ d So, how did you get started?
- ☐ e And what kind of work do you do most?

3 Choose the correct sentence ending, a, b or c.

1 Suzi Marsend ...
   a) looks identical to Marilyn Monroe.
   b) doesn't really sound like Marilyn Monroe.
   c) is a big fan of Marilyn Monroe.

2 She was discovered by a lookalikes agency ...
   a) at a fancy dress party.
   b) in a karaoke pub.
   c) at an audition.

3 She has always wanted to ...
   a) be a Marilyn Monroe lookalike.
   b) be an actress.
   c) run a lookalikes agency.

4 Elvis is ...
   a) better known than Marilyn Monroe.
   b) one of the most requested lookalikes.
   c) Suzi Marsend's favourite singer.

5 Suzi and a friend ...
   a) have just set up a lookalikes agency.
   b) aren't sure if they want to open a lookalikes agency.
   c) are planning to open a lookalikes agency.

4 Complete the summary with the words in bold in the interview.

How to be a celebrity lookalike

The usual route to becoming a lookalike is to send in a portfolio of photos to a lookalike agency. If they like the look of you, they'll (1) _____ with you for (2) _____. You can turn up (3) _____ if you want or you can surprise them as you transform into your celebrity double in front of their very eyes. Always pay attention to detail. Invest in a professional (4) _____ and make-up and make sure you do your homework. Study photos and videos of your chosen celebrity. Concentrate on their (5) _____ and (6) _____, the way they move, the way they talk. These are the details that'll get you the job. But remember, depending on who you (7) _____ for, it can be incredibly (8) _____, so if at first you don't succeed, just keep trying. You'll get there in the end.

🔘 READ & LISTEN

5 🔘 **09** Listen to Reading 3 *How to be a ... celebrity lookalike* on the CD and read the article again.

TWELVIS

Suzi Marsend is small, petite, her hair cut in a short, boyish style. Dressed in jeans and a T-shirt, I'm finding it hard to imagine her as Marilyn Monroe. But she spends up to six days a week playing her double. I asked her about her job and her plans for the future.

How to be a ...
celebrity lookalike

1 _____

Well, it all started as a joke, really. Me and some friends, we went to this fancy dress party and I went as Marilyn, with a cheap **wig** and a second-hand dress. I don't think I looked particularly convincing, but then there was this karaoke bit in the party and everybody had to get up and do something **in character**. And I sang *Happy Birthday Mr President* – you know the one – and quite a few people commented on how I sounded just like her – and well, I really enjoyed the party, but I thought nothing more of it. Till about three weeks later a lookalikes agency managed to **get in touch** with me. Apparently someone from the agency had been at the party and they wanted me to go for **an audition** … it all started from there, really.

2 _____

Off and on for about five years now. It isn't really what I dreamed about doing at drama school, but, hey, it pays the bills and it's actually a lot of fun. And it is acting, too. I don't really think I look that much like Marilyn. The make-up and the professional wigs and the costumes all help obviously, but it's the **mannerisms**, the body language, the **facial expressions**, the voice that are really important. That's what really makes a lookalike a successful lookalike. And I love all that. The acting, getting it right. At the end of the day, that's what I am, an actress playing a part, but I get a kick out of seeing myself dressed up as Marilyn, too. I was never a fan of hers before, but now I am. I've seen so many of her movies so many times! She was a very talented lady.

3 _____

No, not at all. Some do just look incredibly like the celebrity they **double up** for. And that can work really well for photo shoots, you know, adverts, posters, that kind of thing, but they don't usually do quite as well if they have to actually perform. You know, sing, dance, do an interview or whatever.

4 _____

Well, all sorts. I've done stuff from TV ads to wedding parties! I've even done cameos on film sets. Most of the time it's tribute acts, you know, with other lookalikes, too. I mostly do stuff alongside Elvis lookalikes. I think Marilyn and Elvis are probably the two most popular lookalikes, for most events. And I just love singing along to those Elvis tunes! I do other people too, Madonna, Alanis Morrisette, Kylie Minogue, Britney Spears. I've got my own one-woman show, *Blondes Have More Fun*, which I usually tour with for a couple of weeks in the summer.

5 _____

Well, a friend and I have been talking about setting up our own lookalikes agency. It's amazing how much work there is out there for lookalikes, but it's a very **competitive** world and there are a lot of agencies, too. I don't know, we're thinking about it, but we haven't quite plucked up the courage to go it on our own yet. We'll see!

4A | Living in fear

WORD BUILDING

1 Complete the adjectives 1–8 with suffixes from the box.

-ful	-less	-able	-ing	-y

1 distress_____   5 reason_____

2 fear_____   6 relax_____

3 harm_____   7 risk_____

4 pain_____   8 success_____

2 Complete the text with an appropriate form of the words in brackets.

Why is it that some people are born completely
(1) _____ (*fear*) while others are born with
a completely (2) _____ (*reason*) fear of almost
everything? In actual fact, most of our (3) _____
(*anxious*) about the world around us are learnt when we
are very young. Our parents teach us to be (4) _____
(*caution*) about the dangers we face, and we learn from
experience that some things are (5) _____ (*pain*)
and some are not. But the (6) _____ (*possible*)
remains that some of us may be more genetically prone
to fear than others.

EXPLAINING REASONS (*SO THAT, IN ORDER TO, IN CASE, OTHERWISE*)

3 Complete the sentences 1–8 with the phrases a–h.

1 James always tried to make sure that his office could
contact him. Otherwise, ...
2 He bought an expensive mobile phone in order to ...
3 It was important that people could contact him in case ...
4 He chose one with a solar battery so that ...
5 It was a waterproof model so that ...
6 He carried it with him at all times in case ...
7 He slept next to his phone. Otherwise, ...
8 He put the volume on 'extra loud' in order to ...

☐ a be online all the time.
☐ b be sure of hearing it.
☐ c he could take it in the shower.
☐ d he never ran out of power.
☐ e he suffered from terrible anxiety.
☐ f he was afraid of not hearing it.
☐ g it rang.
☐ h there was an emergency.

4 Complete the sentences below the photo.

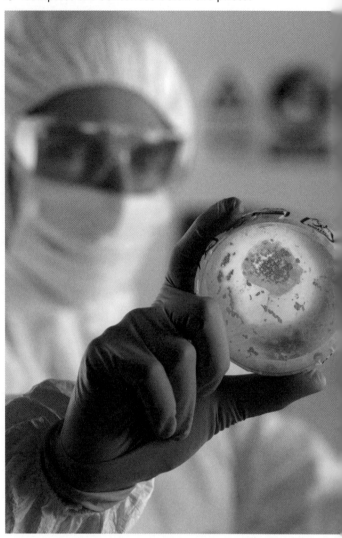

1 He's wearing a mask. Otherwise, ...
2 He's wearing a mask in order to ...
3 He's wearing a mask so that ...
4 He's wearing a mask in case ...

💿 DICTATION

5 💿 **10** Write the sentences that you hear.

1 _____.

2 _____?

3 _____.

4 _____.

5 _____.

6 _____.

4B | Bullying

PRESENT PERFECT & PAST SIMPLE

1 Change the verbs in italics to present perfect where necessary. Make any necessary changes to the word order.

Cyberbullying (1) *is* a relatively new phenomenon. It didn't exist ten years ago. But now it is growing dramatically. More than 35% of teens in the US (2) *experience* some form of cyberbullying through mobile phones or the internet over the last year. Efforts to control cyberbullying (3) *also grow* in schools and colleges. Many schools recently (4) *start* to focus on prevention as well as punishment. These programmes (5) *work* best where they (6) *are* combined with a zero tolerance policy. Reporting bullies to the police (7) *act* as an effective deterrent over the last two years, and authorities (8) *record* a slight reduction in cases of severe bullying. However, the problem certainly (9) *isn't* solved yet – and we'll probably have to wait a long time until it is.

2 Put the verbs in brackets in the past simple or present perfect.

A: (1) _____ (*you / see*) Jayne's blog posting about cyberbullying?

B: No, I (2) _____ (*see*) it. When (3) _____ (*she / post*) it?

A: This morning. I (4) _____ (*just read*) it. It's really powerful – and shocking! (5) _____ (*you / know*) that she was being bullied?

B: Really? I (6) _____ (*have*) no idea!

A: Yes, apparently it all (7) _____ (*start*) about a year ago. She just (8) _____ (*ignore*) it to start with, but then things (9) _____ (*get*) worse and worse …

B: Wow! That's awful. (10) _____ (*she / do*) anything to try and stop it?

A: Yes, she (11) _____ (*find*) out who the bully was about a month ago and she (12) _____ (*try*) writing to the bully at the time, but nothing (13) _____ (*change*).

B: Why doesn't she just go to the police?

A: Well, she (14)_____ (*decide*) to give her bully one last chance. If the bully doesn't stop, she's going to publish their name and report them to the police.

B: I hope it works out for her!

VOCABULARY FROM THE LESSON

3 Complete the words with letters from the box.

a	b	d	d	e	f	m	m
n	r	s	s	u	v	v	

1 _ s s e _ t i _ e

2 _ o s _ y

3 c o n _ i _ e n t

4 d o _ i _ e e r i n g

5 r e _ e r _ e d

6 s _ l f - a s s _ r e _

7 t i _ i d

TRANSLATION

4 Translate the text into your language.

If something dramatic has ever happened to you, how did you react? If you kept a stiff upper lip at the time, the chances are that you have already forgotten quite a lot about it. This may or may not be a good thing, all depending on exactly what it was that happened to you. Some things are best forgotten.

_____

_____

_____

_____

_____

_____

_____

_____

4c | The land of the brave

WORD CLASS

1 Put the words from the box into three groups: nouns, verbs and adjectives. Two of the words can be two different parts of speech.

abolish	abolition	disobedience	disobedient
disobey	free	freedom	liberate	liberation
liberty	move	movement	rebellion
rebellious	religion	religious	

2 Find and correct four mistakes in the sentences.

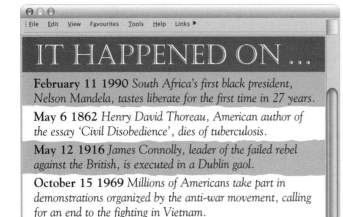

File   Edit   View   Favourites   Tools   Help   Links ➤

IT HAPPENED ON …

February 11 1990 *South Africa's first black president, Nelson Mandela, tastes liberate for the first time in 27 years.*

May 6 1862 *Henry David Thoreau, American author of the essay 'Civil Disobedience', dies of tuberculosis.*

May 12 1916 *James Connolly, leader of the failed rebel against the British, is executed in a Dublin gaol.*

October 15 1969 *Millions of Americans take part in demonstrations organized by the anti-war movement, calling for an end to the fighting in Vietnam.*

November 1 1998 *The European Convention on Human Rights requires all members of the EU to abolish the death penalty.*

December 10 1948 *The United Nations Universal Declaration of Human Rights declares that all people have free of thought, conscience and religious.*

VOCABULARY FROM THE LESSON

3 Complete the headlines with words from the box.

backs	boycott	granted	mass
overturned	racial	regains	spark

1 FOOTBALL HOOLIGANS _____ FIGHTING ACROSS THE CITY

2 Ghana _____ independence from Britain

3 Protestors call for _____ of trade talks

4 Anti-terror law _____

5 _____ resignation of 20 European Commissioners

6 Government _____ new technology

7 Fifty prisoners to be _____ freedom next week

8 POLICE GIVEN NEW POWERS TO FIGHT _____ CRIMES

DICTATION

4 🔊 **11** Write the text that you hear.

_____

_____

_____

_____

_____

_____

_____

_____

4D | Southern snakes

PRESENT PERFECT SIMPLE & CONTINUOUS

1 Three verb forms in italics are **not** possible. Find and delete them.

Snake-charming has (1) *been / been being* illegal in India since 1972. Audiences have also (2) *got / been getting* smaller because people are less afraid of snakes these days. As a result, many snake-charmers have (3) *found / been finding* it very difficult to survive. Millions have (4) *left / been leaving* the profession. Others have (5) *tried / been trying* to persuade the government to change the law. The government has (6) *agreed / been agreeing* that something needs to be done to help these people. It has (7) *looked / been looking* at ways of educating the charmers. But for many charmers, the government's ideas have (8) *come / been coming* too late.

2 Complete the sentences with the verbs in brackets. In each sentence, use both the present perfect simple and the present perfect continuous.

1 For the last few weeks, I _____ a book about genetics, and I _____ about 75 pages. (*read*)

2 We _____ over $200 and we _____ for only two weeks. (*save*)

3 She _____ since she was very young, and she _____ more than five million kilometres. (*drive*)

4 He _____ his job for over ten years, but he _____ a few problems recently. (*have*)

5 The students _____ their exams this week, but they won't get the results until the teachers _____ the marking. (*do*)

3 Put the verbs in brackets into the present perfect simple or present perfect continuous. (Sometimes, both forms are possible.)

For the last nine months, Larry Thomas (1) _____ (*prepare*) for a rodeo in Oklahoma that takes place next month. He (2) _____ (*do*) three separate training courses, each of which lasted two weeks. He (3) _____ (*follow*) a special diet to build up his leg muscles and he (4) _____ (*buy*) a pair of rodeo boots for $8,000. Larry (5) _____ (*look*) forward to the event so much that he (6) _____ (*spend*) over $50,000 to get everything ready. He (7) _____ (*study*) videos of top riders and he (8) _____ (*practise*) on a mechanical training machine. Larry (9) _____ (*leave*) nothing to chance in the lead-up to the big event.

TRANSLATION

4 Translate the text into your language.

A British schoolboy has had the shock of his life after a visit to the lavatory. As the 11-year-old lifted the seat, he was horrified to see a snake raising its head out of the water. The snake, which has still not been caught, is believed to be an American corn snake, which is not dangerous.

4 | Reading

1 Find an example of the words 1–6 in pictures A–C on page 27 and complete the labels a–f.

1
> **framework** /ˈfreɪmwɜːk/ noun [C] ★★
> **2** a structure that supports something and makes it a particular shape: ***The building had a brick base and a metal framework.***

2
> **hot-air balloon** /ˌhɒt ˈeabəˌluːn/ noun [C] an extremely large bag full of hot air, with a basket attached that people can ride through the air in

3
> **paddle** /pædl/ noun [C]
> **1** a short pole that you push into the water in order to move a small boat such as a canoe. It is wide and flat at one or both ends. **4** *AmE* the bat used to play table tennis

4
> **rod** /rɒd/ noun [C] ★★ a long thin bar or stick made of metal, plastic or wood: ***a curtain rod*** **a**. a FISHING ROD

5
> **rudder** /rʌdə/ noun [C] a flat piece of wood or other material at the back of a boat or plane that is moved to change the direction of travel

6
> **wing** /wɪŋ/ noun [C] ★★★
> **1** one of the parts on a bird, insect or bat that move up and down and allow it to fly. Birds have two wings, but insects have either two or four wings.
> **2** one of the long flat parts on both sides of a plane that allow it to fly

© Mike Baldwin / Cornered

www.CartoonStock.com

'Of course it's safe.
Even has an airbag.'

2 Read the article again. Answer the questions with the name of the aviator A–D (A: the Marquis de Bacqueville, B: Jacques Charles, C: Vincent de Groof, D: Monsieur Goupil ...).

Which early aviator ...
1 built a machine that has possibly never been tested?
2 crashed into a boat?
3 died?
4 had to pedal very fast in order to take off?
5 left his home country to make his attempt?
6 lost one machine but found success in another?
7 used a balloon to lift his machine into the air?
8 was almost too scared to make his attempt?
9 was observed by a large crowd of people?

3 Organize the words and phrases from the stories into three groups of meaning.

> coming down   connecting   descent
> device   fitted to   flying machine
> invention   landing   linked to

4 In what ways would your life be different if planes had not been invented?

🔘 READ & LISTEN

5 🔘 **12** Listen to Reading 4 *Flying lessons* on the CD and read the article again.

Flying lessons

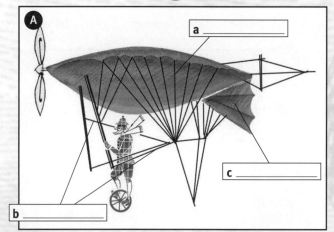

A

a _____

b _____

c _____

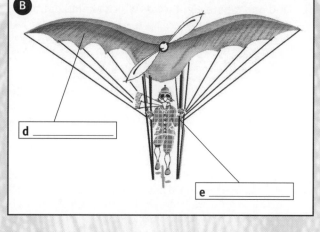

B

d _____

e _____

1 One of the most courageous birdmen was 62-year-old French nobleman, the Marquis de Bacqueville, who, in 1742, prepared to fly across the River Seine in Paris with paddles fitted to his arms and legs. At the last moment, he had second thoughts about his invention and asked a servant to try it out first. The servant, sensing that refusal would mean unemployment, diplomatically pointed out that a valet could not possibly precede his master. The Marquis did not know how to reply and, with a big crowd waiting below, realized he had no choice. He would have to do it himself. He jumped out of a window on the top floor of his house and began flapping his paddles vigorously. He fell to the ground like a stone, narrowly missing the pavement, but landing instead on a pile of old clothes in a washerwoman's boat. The washerwoman had stopped her boat on the riverbank in order to enjoy the spectacle. The clothes cushioned the Marquis's fall and he suffered nothing more than a broken leg.

2 On 27 August 1783, Jacques Alexandre César Charles released a 3.6m diameter unmanned balloon from Champ-de-Mars, Paris. It made a 45-minute flight to Gonesse, but, on landing, it was attacked and destroyed by violent villagers who thought it was a monster. Their fears were reinforced by a curious smell coming from a hole in the balloon. Three months later, Charles and his friend, Nicolas Robert, lifted off from The Tuileries in Paris in a hydrogen-filled balloon. Coming down safely in a town over forty kilometres away, Charles and Robert joined the Montgolfier brothers as the world's first aviators.

3 Few flying machines were as bizarre as the invention of Belgian shoemaker, Vincent de Groof. His equipment – 'a device with bat-like wings'– was part flapper, part parachute. The framework was made of wood and the 12m wings were covered with waterproof silk, and controlled by three wooden levers worked by the arms and legs. The tail, also covered with strong silk, was 6m long. On 9 July 1874, de Groof planned a flight over London. He was to be taken to an altitude of 300m by balloon and then released. The ascent went well; the descent was less successful. Released over the Thames, de Groof and his machine crashed into a street in Chelsea when the wing frame failed. De Groof was killed.

4 The 1870s also saw Monsieur A. Goupil's aerial velocipede. The Frenchman's machine resembled a unicycle under a zeppelin. The balloon-type structure was made of wood, covered with silk, and weighed 100kg. The aeronaut stood on the pedals of the unicycle, which was linked to the balloon by connecting rods. From this position, he operated the pedals and a rudder. A description of M. Goupil's invention in the *Chronique Industrielle* explained: 'As the machine's speed increases, its weight decreases, as a result of the increase in the vertical reaction of the current. It should then ascend and remain in the air.' It is not known whether Monsieur Goupil's aerial velocipede ever passed its first test.

C

f _____

5A | Modern art

NARRATIVE TENSES

1 Find and delete eight words which should not be in the text.

THE ART FILES

Staff at FBI Headquarters in Washington DC had never given much thought to art. But, with the realization that the country was been losing as much as $2 billion each year, the FBI did set up the Art Crime Team in 2004. Twelve special agents were joined the team after they had been received special training in art crime. The agents had began to track down a long list of missing art works. By the end of their first year of operations, they had being recovered items worth over $50 million. These were included a self-portrait by Rembrandt which did had been stolen from the National Museum in Stockholm.

2 Put the verbs in brackets into the past simple, the past continuous or the past perfect.

Rembrandt (1) _____ (*live*) in modest accommodation in Amsterdam when this self-portrait (2) _____ (*be*) painted. He (3) _____ (*have*) to sell his family house and his financial problems (4) _____ (*grow*). He (5) _____ (*be*) bankrupt because he (6) _____ (*spend*) too much on his collection of old prints. Four of his children (7) _____ (*already die*) and, at 53 years of age, Rembrandt's own health (8) _____ (*begin*) to fail, although he (9) _____ (*live*) for another ten years.

ART

3 Find thirteen words connected with art in the word search.

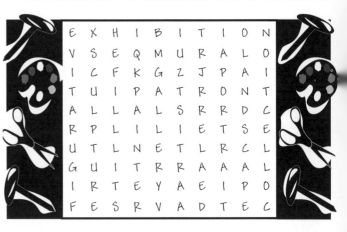

E	X	H	I	B	I	T	I	O	N
V	S	E	Q	M	U	R	A	L	O
I	C	F	K	G	Z	J	P	A	I
T	U	I	P	A	T	R	O	N	T
A	L	L	A	L	S	R	R	D	C
R	P	L	I	L	I	E	T	S	E
U	T	L	N	E	T	L	R	C	L
G	U	I	T	R	R	A	A	A	L
I	R	T	E	Y	A	E	I	P	O
F	E	S	R	V	A	D	T	E	C

4 Complete the sentences with a word from the word search in exercise 3.

1 The world's most hard-working _____ was probably Picasso, who produced hundreds of thousands of paintings, prints, illustrations and other work.

2 The world's most valuable _____ of private art is probably the J Paul Getty Museum in Los Angeles.

3 The world's largest _____, made of steel and plastic by Anish Kapoor, is 150 metres long.

4 The world's most famous _____ painter is probably Diego Rivera, whose work can be seen on the walls of the Detroit Institute of Arts.

5 The world's most expensive _____, a picture of a woman by Gustav Klimt, cost over $130 million.

6 In the world's biggest art theft, $500 million worth of paintings were stolen from a _____ in Holland.

7 The world's highest price paid for a _____ was $60 million for some fruit, a curtain and a jug by Cézanne.

🔘 DICTATION

5 🔘 **13** Write the text that you hear.

_____

_____

_____

_____

_____

5B | Priceless!

-EVER WORDS

1 Complete the sentences with phrases from the box. More than one answer is possible.

did that	happens	he was
you are	you do	you say

1 Wherever _____, he certainly wasn't here.

2 Whatever _____, don't do that!

3 Whatever _____, this must remain a secret between us.

4 Whatever _____ is fine with me.

5 Whoever _____ is going to regret it soon.

6 Whoever _____, come out of there with your hands up.

2 Complete the sentences with *however, whatever, whenever, wherever* or *whoever*.

1 _____ much that costs, I want to buy it.

2 _____ told you that needs their head examining.

3 You can have _____ colour you like.

4 Put it _____ you want, but not in this room, please.

5 _____ you look at me like that, I know you're going to say something.

6 I'll be happy with _____ you want, my dear.

7 _____ I am, I'm always thinking of you.

EVALUATING

3 Complete the dialogues with words from the box.

fortune	masterpiece	priceless	redeeming
rubbish	valuable	worth	worthless

- It says here that this is probably his (1) _____.
- Really? It must be worth a (2) _____.
- Yes, absolutely (3) _____, I should think. Even his early works are extremely (4) _____.
- Really? Not my kind of thing really.

THEY BOTH BITTERLY REGRETTED LYING TO THE DATING AGENCY ABOUT AN INTEREST IN ART.

MIKE TURNER

www.CartoonStock.com

- What a load of (5) _____!
- Yeah. Just a couple of lines and a badly-drawn bird. No (6) _____ features at all.
- It's amazing that people buy this stuff. It's absolutely (7) _____.
- Yes. It says $35,000, but it's (8) _____ nothing.

TRANSLATION

4 Translate the two dialogues in exercise 3 into your language.

5c | A good read

PAST PERFECT CONTINUOUS

1 Rearrange the words to make sentences.

1 been had her husband trying job get
   to new a .

   _____

2 at been had she sleeping the time .

   _____

3 been for had hours in she standing
   sun the .

   _____

4 about ages been for had it she thinking .

   _____

5 been for four had she trying years .

   _____

6 been crowd for growing had hours the .

   _____

7 been children dinner eating the front had
   in of the their TV .

   _____

2 Match the sentences a–g to the sentences in exercise 1.

☐ a Helen decided to take early retirement.
☐ b It was no surprise that she fainted.
☐ c Mandy was relieved when he finally succeeded.
☐ d She heard absolutely nothing.
☐ e The atmosphere was electric.
☐ f There were stains all over the sofa.
☐ g She was delighted to learn that she was
       finally pregnant.

3 Put the verbs in brackets into the past perfect simple
   or continuous. Use the past perfect simple a maximum
   of four times.

Arundhati Roy, the Indian writer and political activist,
(1) _____ (*only just turn*) 35 when she won
the Man Booker prize for her first novel, *The God of
Small Things.* Prior to this international success, Roy
(2) _____ (*write*) movie scripts. Her work in the
movie industry (3) _____ (*start*) when she was in her
early 20s. She (4) _____ (*cycle*) down the street one
day when she was spotted by the film director, Pradeep
Krishen. In India, she (5) _____ (*become*) reasonably
well-known for her TV and cinema work by the time she
was about 30. Then, in the early 1990s, she found herself
in court after publishing a film review in which she
(6) _____ (*criticize*) a popular film about the 'Bandit
Queen', Phoolan Devi. Roy decided to move out of the
public eye. Four years later, she reappeared. During this
time, Roy (7) _____ (*work*) on her first novel. With
the fame that she (8) _____ (*win*) with the prize-
winning book, Roy decided to abandon fiction and the
cinema. She devoted her life to political and environmental
causes. In January 2000,
she was arrested in the
Narmada Valley, where she
(9) _____ (*protest*)
against the building of a
dam. In 2010 she toured the
universities of the United
States speaking out against
corruption and exploitation
as she (10) _____ (*do*)
for the last ten years.

🔊 DICTATION

4 🔊 **14** Write the text that you hear.

_____

_____

_____

_____

_____

_____

_____

_____

5D | Bookworm

PHRASAL VERBS 1

1 Complete the sentences 1–6 with the phrases a–f.

1 I don't know how she comes up with ...
2 It's not easy living up to ...
3 People really take to ...
4 The publishers turned down ...
5 With the money from her fifth book, she set up ...
6 She moved out of the city to bring up ...

- [ ] a a charitable foundation.
- [ ] b her children.
- [ ] c her first attempt to write a novel.
- [ ] d her reputation.
- [ ] e so many original ideas.
- [ ] f the characters in her novels.

2 Replace the phrases a–f in exercise 1 with a pronoun (*it* or *them*) and rewrite the complete sentences.

VOCABULARY FROM THE LESSON

3 Choose the best word to complete the sentences, a, b or c.

1 She dared to _____ up at him one final time before fainting into his arms.

   a) dangle   b) falter   c) glance

2 They don't come any better than this. A real _____ that will keep you turning the pages all night.

   a) classic   b) network   c) regime

3 It is understood that the offenders will be kept in a _____ centre until they appear before the judge.

   a) colossal   b) detention   c) pretentious

4 The panel of judges will select six entrants for the _____ list, before choosing the final winner next month.

   a) short   b) slot   c) sting

5 A tireless campaigner for women's rights, she has _____ thousands of women with her TV broadcasts and best-selling books.

   a) inspired   b) nominated   c) suspended

6 I don't know what we'd have done without her. She was an absolute _____, almost like an unpaid maid.

   a) clove   b) god-send   c) jug

7 Brighten up your hallway with this period-style gold umbrella-holder. _____ one now while stocks last.

   a) Grab   b) Nosedive   c) Pierce

4 Match the sentences 1–7 in exercise 3 to the text types a–g.

- [ ] a a biography
- [ ] b a book review
- [ ] c a news item
- [ ] d a personal letter
- [ ] e a romantic novel
- [ ] f an advertisement
- [ ] g competition rules

TRANSLATION

5 Translate the text into your language.

My mother did not tell me they were coming. Afterwards she said she did not want me to appear nervous. I was surprised, for I thought she knew me well. Strangers would think I was calm. I did not cry as a baby. Only my mother would note the tightness along my jaw, the widening of my already wide eyes.

(Girl with a Pearl Earring, by Tracy Chevalier, *chapter 1)*

_____

_____

_____

_____

_____

_____

_____

5 | Reading

1 Answer the questions.

1 What kind of photos do you like taking?
2 What, in your opinion, is the secret of taking good photos?
3 Is it necessary to have a good camera to take a good photo? Why or why not?

2 Read the article and choose the correct sentence endings, a, b or c.

1 If Robert Capa were still alive, he might be surprised to find his work in art galleries because …
   a) he did not think highly of his own work.
   b) he did not think of himself as an artist.
   c) he had to change his name.

2 He moved to Paris …
   a) because it was hard to make a living in Berlin.
   b) for political reasons.
   c) to be with his girlfriend.

3 Capa's time in Spain was …
   a) both good and bad for him.
   b) the high point of his life.
   c) financially very rewarding.

4 His experience in the Second World War …
   a) helped him get over the death of his fiancée.
   b) meant that he did not have much time for photography.
   c) were very unhappy.

5 Capa wanted to get close to the fighting …
   a) because he enjoyed the danger.
   b) because he was not afraid of death.
   c) in order to get a good record of the action.

6 After the Second World War, Capa …
   a) became more involved in the business side of photography.
   b) did not want to take any more war photographs.
   c) went to live in Vietnam.

3 Read the article again and insert the sentences 1–6 in the spaces a–f.

1 Friedmann only learnt of her death after reading a newspaper article.
2 His reputation as an artist has never been higher.
3 Many of the men on board were killed.
4 One magazine learnt of the deception, but continued to buy the photographs.
5 Some, however, were unfortunately lost in the fighting.
6 There was a tragic inevitability to Capa's death.

4 Explain in your own words the words in italics in the phrases below.

1 *grace* the walls (paragraph 1)

   _____

2 *struggled* to make a living (paragraph 2)

   _____

3 *catapulted* Capa to fame (paragraph 3)

   _____

4 *dwell* on his unhappiness (paragraph 4)

   _____

5 the *thick* of the action (paragraph 5)

   _____

6 *cover* the war (paragraph 6)

   _____

🔊 READ & LISTEN

5 🔊 **15** Listen to Reading 5 *Close up: Robert Capa* on the CD and read the article again.

CLOSE UP: ROBERT CAPA

1 One of the biggest names in the history of photography, Robert Capa, was, in fact, the pseudonym of the Hungarian-born Endre (or Andrei) Friedmann. Capa saw himself as a journalist, but his pictures now grace the walls of art galleries around the world. (a) _____

2 Leaving his home town of Budapest to study in Berlin, Friedmann had to leave the German capital in 1933 when the Nazis took power. He moved to Paris, where he struggled to make a living as a photographer until he met his fiancée, a Polish refugee, Gerda Taro. Together, they invented 'Robert Capa - a rich and secretive American photographer' who would only sell his work for high prices. Gerda acted as a sales representative, while Friedmann pretended to be Capa's technical helper. (b) _____

3 Capa's new-found success led to him being offered a contract in 1936 to cover the Civil War in Spain. While there, he took the now-legendary photo of a militia man at the moment of his death. The picture catapulted Capa to fame, but shortly afterwards Gerda was killed in the fighting. (c) _____

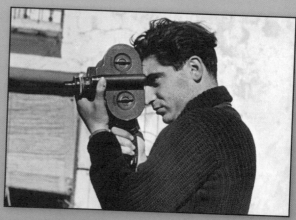

4 Capa buried his grief in his work and, with the outbreak of the Second World War, he had little time to dwell on his unhappiness. Working as a photojournalist, he parachuted into Sicily, was among the first American troops to land in France on the beaches of Normandy and witnessed the liberation of Paris. Many of Capa's most memorable images date from this period. (d) _____

5 Capa was a fearless, even reckless, man and was described by one of his friends as the world's worst driver. In all of his assignments, he threw himself into the thick of the action. It was the only way, he believed, to take good pictures. In Normandy, he was only a few metres from death when his landing-ship was hit by a shell. (e) _____

6 At the end of the war, Capa returned to Paris and, with his friends Henri Cartier-Bresson and David 'Chim' Seymour, he founded the Magnum photographic agency, which is still one of the most well-known agencies in the world. He concentrated on building the business, but in 1954 he accepted his final assignment for *Life* magazine to cover the war in Vietnam. At the age of 40, he lost his life after stepping on a landmine, as he attempted to get closer to the horrors of war that he had spent his life documenting. (f) _____

6A | The vote

REAL & UNREAL CONDITIONS

1 Insert the words in brackets in the sentences.

1 Anyone can become the president of the US they want to badly enough and they're ready to work hard to get what they want. (*provided*)
2 Don't enter politics you know exactly why you're doing it and what you want out of it. (*unless*)
3 He might have won the election he hadn't lost his temper and insulted his opponent live on TV. (*if*)
4 I would only enter politics I could guarantee the privacy of my wife and children. (*so long as*)
5 I'll give up my post as governor I can run for president. (*on condition that*)
6 He would never have been so successful it hadn't been for his wife. (*if*)
7 I would never, ever consider a life in politics, of course, I was asked to. (*unless*)
8 You want a career in politics, you'll have to be prepared to give up everything else, friends, family and all your free time. (*if*)

2 Which sentences in exercise 1 are real and which are unreal conditions?

3 Correct the grammatical errors in the quotations.

1 If you pick up a starving dog and make him prosperous, he did not bite you. This is the principal difference between a man and a dog. (Mark Twain)
2 If we couldn't laugh, we'll all go insane. (Jimmy Buffet)

3 There is a theory which states that if ever anybody will discover exactly what the Universe is for and why it is here, it will instantly disappear and be replaced by something even more bizarre and unexplicable. (Douglas Adams)
4 Americans will put up with anything provided it didn't block traffic. (Dan Rather)
5 Nobody would have believed in you unless you believe in yourself. (Liberace)
6 Oh, I don't blame Congress. If I have $600 billion at my disposal, I'd be irresponsible, too. (Lichty and Wagner)

🔘 DICTATION

4 🔘 **16** Write the sentences that you hear.

1 _____
   _____
2 _____
   _____
3 _____
   _____
4 _____
   _____
5 _____
   _____

'What's also amazing is that their policies are almost identical ...'

6B | Women in politics

I WISH & IF ONLY

1 Match the sentences 1–6 to the phrases a–f.

1 I'm broke, homeless and divorced.
2 I'm not satisfied with your work.
3 I'm sorry I can't promise you that.
4 It's a pity I don't know any politicians.
5 Unfortunately, I never worked much at school.
6 Why did I say something so stupid?

☐ a I wish I hadn't.
☐ b I wish I were.
☐ c I wish I weren't.
☐ d If only I could.
☐ e If only I did.
☐ f If only I had.

2 Put the verbs in brackets into the correct form.

1 **A:** He seemed such an honest, trustworthy person.

   B: Yes. If only we _____ (*know*) then what we know now.

2 **A:** I'm really missing you.

   B: Me, too. I wish you _____ (*be*) here.

3 **A:** I told your husband everything.

   B: You know what? I really wish you _____ (*not do*) that.

4 **A:** It's a beautiful view, isn't it?

   B: Yes, it is. But I wish it _____ (*not rain*).

5 **A:** So, you had a good time last night?

   B: Yes! If only you _____ (*be*) there. You'd have loved it.

ELECTIONS

3 Complete the sentences with an appropriate word.

1 In New Zealand, there are always at least seven Maori M _ _ _ _ _ _ of Parliament.

2 In some European elections, the t _ _ _ _ _ _ has been as low as 20%.

3 Many British schools are used as p _ _ _ _ _ _ stations on election days.

4 Outer Delhi, the world's largest parliamentary c _ _ _ _ _ _ _ _ _ _ _, has over three million voters.

5 Over 150,000 Londoners could not understand how to fill in the b _ _ _ _ _ papers in a recent local election.

6 The American Prohibition Party (which wants to prohibit all alcohol) has nominated a c _ _ _ _ _ _ _ _ in every US presidential election since 1872.

7 There are still a few countries where g _ _ _ _ _ _ elections do not take place.

VOCABULARY FROM THE LESSON

4 Complete the text with words from the box.

committed	fight	involved	represented
run	set	step	voted

Many Hollywood stars have been (1) _____ in political action of one kind or another. Some, like Ronald Reagan, (2) _____ their sights on, and get, the top job. Others, like Clint Eastwood, are happy to (3) _____ for office in smaller jobs – Eastwood was mayor of Carmel in California for two years before deciding to (4) _____ aside, even though 72% of the electorate had (5) _____ for him. Still others, like Danny De Vito or Robert De Niro, give tens of thousands of dollars to help their political friends (6) _____ elections. The Democrats are generally better (7) _____ in Hollywood than the Republicans, but there are many, like Bruce Willis or Mel Gibson, who are (8) _____ to the Republican cause.

TRANSLATION

5 Translate the poem into your language.

If only I could know you
I've watched you now so long
If only I could know your name
And know your favorite song

If only I could know you
I see you every day
But any time you look at me
I turn and look away

I wonder if you've noticed me
I try hard not to stare
But even if you've seen my face
You'll never see I care

Fred Hobbs

6c | Politically incorrect

EMBARRASSMENT

1 Put the lines in the correct order.

- ☐ ashamed, or even in some cases
- ☐ *1* How do you usually cope with acute
- ☐ bright red? Some people are not at all self-
- ☐ humiliated at the slightest mistake.
- ☐ embarrassment? Do you laugh it off or go
- ☐ situations without even blushing. But other people squirm
- ☐ uncomfortably and feel acutely
- ☐ conscious and can brush off embarrassing

SHOULD HAVE

2 Choose the more appropriate response, a or b, to the sentences 1–6.

1 It's my birthday.
   a) I shouldn't have told you.
   b) You should have told us!

2 We've organized a surprise party for you.
   a) I should have guessed!
   b) I should have learnt by now.

3 I'm sorry. I've completely forgotten his number.
   a) You should have written it down.
   b) You shouldn't have bothered.

4 We've brought you a little present.
   a) It shouldn't have happened.
   b) Oh, you shouldn't have!

5 Come on, you dirty rat!
   a) I should have seen it coming.
   b) You shouldn't have said that!

6 I don't care if it was my fault.
   a) You should have apologized.
   b) You should have seen it.

7 Why the secret?
   a) I'm sorry. I should have mentioned it before.
   b) I don't know. I really shouldn't have.

8 I must speak to the bank manager later today.
   a) Why should you have done that?
   b) Shouldn't you have done that yesterday?

3 Read the text and write six sentences about it, which include *should have* or *shouldn't have*.

In the 1870s, the US government fought a war against the Lakota tribes whose land the government wanted to take. Breaking a treaty with the Lakota, the US forces attacked. Colonel George Custer was made leader of a cavalry division despite the fact that he had a very poor service record. During one campaign, Custer's cavalry advanced much faster than the foot-soldiers and the rest of the army. Coming across a combined force of Lakota and Cheyenne, Custer ignored his orders not to attack. He also refused to listen to the advice of his scouts. Custer was almost certainly motivated by the thought that a heroic victory would get him into the White House. Even though he knew he had fewer soldiers than the enemy, he divided his men into three groups in order to attack the village on the Little Big Horn River. The Native Americans of Chief Sitting Bull were waiting for them. None of the 210 men of the Seventh Cavalry survived. It was even worse for the Lakota. Within a year the whole tribe had been destroyed.

🔘 DICTATION

4 🔘 **17** Write the text that you hear.

_____

_____

_____

_____

_____

_____

_____

_____

6D | Politically correct

-ISMS

1 Choose the best description, a or b, for each slogan 1–5.

1 a) the anti-sexist b) the sexist
2 a) the elitist b) the idealist
3 a) the racist b) the socialist
4 a) the optimist b) the pacifist
5 a) the ageist b) the realist

2 Match the words from the box to the definitions 1–6.

> anarchist   atheist   capitalist   fatalist
> individualist   materialist

1 someone who believes that God does not exist
   _____

2 someone who believes that there should be no
   government or laws _____

3 someone who believes that you cannot prevent things
   from happening, especially bad things _____

4 someone who believes that money and possessions are
   the most important aspects of human existence
   _____

5 someone who does things in their own way without
   worrying about what other people think or do
   _____

6 someone who is successful in business or invests
   money in business for profit _____

ASKING FOR & GIVING CLARIFICATION

3 Complete the dialogue with words from the box.

> basically   follow   know   mean
> meant   point   suggesting   words

A: It's a very serious situation, you know.

B: Yes, I know, I (1) _____. But what are you
(2) _____? That I should apologize?

A: Well, maybe it's time that you thought about doing
something else.

B: I don't (3) _____. What do you (4) _____?

A: Well, you know, look around. Consider your options.

B: I see. So, (5) _____, you're saying that
I should resign?

A: No, that's not what I (6) _____. My
(7) _____ is simply that you should seriously
consider your position.

B: In other (8) _____, resign.

A: Yes.

TRANSLATION

4 Translate the text into your language.

These babies are born with equal opportunities, but the
educational and career expectations for boys and girls are
different. By the time they grow up, the boy will be earning
on average 17.5% more than the girl.

Women have as good or better qualifications than men, but
often their skills are not as valued as men's and their career
progression is slower. This results in an average gender pay
gap of 17.5% in the European Union.

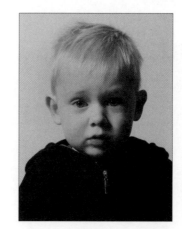

6 | Reading

1 Read the article below. Then decide, on a scale from 1 (very honest) to 10 (very corrupt): how corrupt are politicians in your country? (You can find out more at the website that is mentioned in the article.)

According to *Transparency International*, a global organization that is fighting corruption, three-quarters of all countries in the world have a serious political corruption problem. The three most common types of corruption are:

■ Bribery

Politicians demand money (or accept money when it is offered) in exchange for the use of their official powers. They may, for example, use their position to give a business advantage to a client or promise to vote in a certain way.

■ Embezzlement

Embezzlement is stealing from the government. It can take many forms, including the use of government employees for private work, or exaggerating the expenses that politicians can claim for doing their work.

■ Patronage

Politicians sometimes use their power to provide jobs for their friends, family and supporters, instead of appointing more qualified or more experienced people.

2 Match the headlines to the news stories.

1

MP JAILED FOR 18 MONTHS

2

PARTY LEADERS CALL FOR MEMBERS TO GIVE BACK EXPENSES MONEY

3

Telegraph leaks information on MPs' expenses

4

TORY MP CLAIMS £2,000 FOR CLEANING HIS MOAT

3 Read the stories again and decide if these sentences are true (T) or false (F). Correct the false sentences.

1 The expenses scandal has only targeted one of the main political parties.
2 The scandal was started by a newspaper.
3 A former prime minister released the confidential information.
4 Some MPs were told to pay back the money that they had been given.
5 David Chaytor is not the only MP to be charged with false accounting.
6 Only minor political figures have been involved in the scandal.

4 Find words or phrases in the texts that mean ...

1 made information public (text A) _____
2 the money you pay to maintain a house in good order and condition (text B) _____
3 had their reputation damaged by something (text C) _____
4 an examination of financial accounts (text C) _____
5 be found guilty by a court of law (text D) _____
6 claimed formally (in a court of law) to be guilty or innocent (text D) _____

5 Match the sentences 1–4 to the end of the texts A–D.

1 It has also been claimed that he used public money to pay for a piano tuner and for work to be done on his stables.
2 All three parties agree that action must be taken, and be seen to be taken, as soon as possible.
3 A Labour party spokesman told journalists that the former MP had been formally excluded from the party.
4 Key figures from both the government and the opposition have also been named and more is yet to come.

💿 READ & LISTEN

6 💿 **18** Listen to Reading 6 *MPs' expenses scandal* on the CD and read the news stories again.

MPs' expenses scandal

A   *The Daily Telegraph* today released confidential information about top MPs' exaggerated expense claims. The article reports that hundreds of MPs have been making false claims at the taxpayers' expense, some for thousands of pounds, and mostly connected with second homes. The source has not been named, but the information is being taken very seriously. Former prime minister Tony Blair is among those accused of abusing the MPs' expenses system.

B   It's day five of the expenses scandal and Conservative MP and former agriculture minister, Douglas Hogg, has been accused of making various claims for thousands of pounds' worth of maintenance work at his country estate in Lincolnshire where he lives with his family. Under the current rules, MPs can claim expenses for the reasonable running costs of two homes, one in their constituency and one in London when they are attending parliament, but the expenses do not normally cover the maintenance for a stately home complete with a moat! It seems that he also claimed £18,000 for a gardener, as well as contributions for the salary of a full-time housekeeper.

C   Members of all the three main political parties have been accused of corruption. Party leaders, all tainted by the on-going expenses scandal, have been quick to call on their members to pay back expenses or face disciplinary action. The Tories are threatening to expel any MPs who refuse to pay back excessive expenses. The Liberal Democrats are asking their MPs to hand back profits made from selling properties that were subsidized by the parliamentary expenses system and the Labour leader has called for an independent, external audit on all expense claims made in the last four years.

D   David Chaytor is the first MP to be convicted following the expenses scandal. The former Labour MP pleaded guilty to three charges of false accounting and was sentenced to eighteen months in prison. He admitted making false claims for more than £18,000 and has already agreed to pay back the money. His lawyer had pleaded for the sentence to be suspended, but the judge believed that it was important that the former MP be seen to serve a prison sentence in an attempt to win back public trust in the judicial system. It is likely that other MPs will soon be following in Chaytor's footsteps.

Glossary

moat *n* a deep, wide hole that surrounds a castle

country estate *n* a large country house with land around it

stately home *n* the country home of an aristocrat

suspended sentence *n* the person does not have to go to prison unless they commit another offence during the term of the sentence

7A | Green issues

The environment

1 Choose the best words to complete the text.

Have you noticed how it's getting hotter every summer? You can't tell me it's not connected with global (1) *fuels / warming*. It's all those greenhouse (2) *gases / energy* that are warming the planet. Part of the problem is that there are too many cars and the exhaust (3) *organic / fumes* are polluting everything. A few (4) *global / wind* farms or a bit of (5) *hydro-electric / emission* power won't stop the climate (6) *changing / fossil*. Anyway, we've started eating organic (7) *consumption / food* in our family and we recycle everything.

Vocabulary from the lesson

2 Combine words from each box to make compound nouns.

car organic	areas illnesses
chronic coastal	bags ink
carrier printer	crops tyres
plant	dyes

3 Complete the sentences with a pair of words in exercise 2.

1 More and more farmers are growing _____ to meet the demand for safe food.

2 Many people who live in _____ are worried about their homes if sea levels rise.

3 Air pollution can be responsible for lung disease, asthma and other _____.

4 Billions of plastic _____ are given away by shops and supermarkets every year.

5 _____ are not always safer than chemical or industrially produced ones.

6 The rubber of _____ gives off poisonous fumes when it burns.

7 Some companies sell printers very cheaply, so that you have to buy their expensive _____.

🔘 Dictation

4 🔘 **19** Write the text that you hear.

_____

_____

_____

_____

_____

_____

_____

_____

_____

(extract from *United Nations Framework Convention on Climate Change*)

7B | Green houses

FUTURES REVIEW

1 Choose the best verb form to complete the sentences.

1 It looks like it's *being / going to be* another beautiful day today.
2 Sea levels *are rising / will rise* dramatically over the next 50 years.
3 Local governments *are meeting / will meet* to discuss plans to improve recycling systems this weekend.
4 Water consumption *is not decreasing / will not decrease* until excess water usage is made punishable by law.
5 The neighbours decided that *they're going to have / they'll have* solar panels fitted on the kitchen roof.
6 That looks heavy! Let me help. You get that end and *I'm grabbing / I'll grab* this end.

2 Change six of the verbs in italics to a more appropriate form with *going to* + infinitive, present continuous or present simple.

A: (1) *Will you fix* that tap or not? And if so, when?
B: Yes, (2) *I'll do* it soon. I promise.
A: Because my father (3) *will come* round for lunch tomorrow. (4) *I'll ask* him to bring his tools, if you like.
B: No, that's OK. (5) *I'll do* it as soon as (6) *I'll have* a spare moment.
A: And when (7) *will that be*?
B: Well, not today because (8) *I'll have* an appointment with the doctor at four.
A: But (9) *that'll only last* half an hour.
B: Yes, but after that, (10) *I'll see* Winston for a drink.
A: Oh right. And (11) *will you do* anything special tomorrow morning?
B: No, (12) *I'll probably have* a lie-in.
A: You know what? (13) *I'll get* my father to do it.

EXPRESSIONS WITH *MAKE*

3 Complete the sentences with prepositions from the box.

for	of	to	with

1 I promise I'll make more time _____ you in the future.
2 I think I could make do _____ very little if I had to.
3 I'm sorry, but it doesn't make any sense at all _____ me.
4 It looks like make or break _____ me at work in the next few days.
5 We should always try to make the most _____ what we've got.
6 Let's make it easy _____ everyone to understand.
7 Why do you always make a point _____ being late?
8 It doesn't make any difference _____ me.

TRANSLATION

4 Translate the text into your language.

GREENPEACE

Greenpeace exists because this fragile earth deserves a voice. It needs solutions. It needs change. It needs action.

Greenpeace is a non-profit organization, with a presence in more than 40 countries across Europe, the Americas, Asia and the Pacific.

To maintain its independence, Greenpeace does not accept donations from governments or corporations, but relies on contributions from individual supporters and foundation grants.

7c | Lifestyle changes

FUTURE PERFECT & FUTURE CONTINUOUS

1 Insert the missing words (*be* and *have*) in sentences 1–7.

1 Heather is training to become a life coach. As soon as she's qualified, she'll looking for work.
2 But before she earns anything, she'll spent over $1,000 on her training.
3 She'll having her next class at 3 o'clock on Tuesday afternoon.
4 After that, she'll done nearly two-thirds of the course.
5 She'll taking her final exam in December.
6 If she passes that, she'll starting her 'experience programme' immediately afterwards.
7 She hopes she will completed all her training by next summer.

2 Look at the diary page. Write three sentences in each of the following ways.

1 *She'll be …*
2 *She'll have …*

Week 13	**March-April**
─────── TODAY ▶	**Monday 27**
11.15 - 11.45 Coaching observation	
NB Start working on portfolio!	
	Tuesday 28
2.30 - 3.30 Role play workshop	
4.30 - 6.00 Lecture: Principles of Listening	
	Wednesday 29
4.30 - 6.00 Lecture: Active Listening	
	Thursday 30
11.15 - 11.45 Coaching observation	
	Friday 31
3.30 - 4.30 Role play workshop	
5.00 Hand in portfolio!	
	Saturday 1
8.30 Class meal (L'Oreille à la Bouche)	
	Sunday 2
Start work on assignment 5!!	

VOCABULARY FROM THE LESSON

3 Choose the best word a–c to complete the sentences.

1 I won't say who told me, but it was a _____ friend.

   a) blanket   b) glove   c) mutual

2 I'm afraid it's simply a question of will _____.

   a) force   b) power   c) strength

3 He's trying to get in _____ before he goes skiing.

   a) fit   b) shape   c) step

4 There's no point having plans unless you put them into _____.

   a) action   b) lifestyle   c) pinpoint

5 Let's _____ up an action plan and then decide who does what.

   a) call   b) draw   c) pull

6 Even if you don't _____ all your goals, it's still worth the effort.

   a) get   b) have   c) reach

7 I think it's time we cleared the _____ between us.

   a) air   b) barrier   c) block

8 I appreciate your _____ support, but money would also help.

   a) approve   b) moral   c) supplement

🔘 DICTATION

4 🔘 **20** Write the dialogue that you hear.

A: _____.

B: _____.

A: _____.

B: _____.

A: _____.

B: _____.

A: _____.

7D | Trends

GIVING EXAMPLES

1 Put the lines in the correct order.

☐ as yoga or t'ai chi. But I'll make the changes gradually. I may start, for

☐ example, by only watching four hours of TV a day.

[1] I'm seeing a life coach because, among other

☐ instance, might be quite fun. I plan to change my diet and cut down on chips, in

☐ particular. We're also talking about other things I can do, such

☐ things, I want to lead a healthier lifestyle. I'm going to give up some of my hobbies, like

☐ video games, and take up a sport. Squash, for

2 Delete five expressions in italics that do not belong to the text.

If you want to find out about the future, there are many people, *among other things*, who can help you. You can turn, *for example*, to the horoscope pages of *such as* the newspaper where you can find out about your love life, *in particular*. For more serious information, you can dip into the writing of well-known prophets *such as* Nostradamus or use magical books *like* the I Ching, *to name but a few*. But if you're really serious *for instance* about the future, you can take a course, *in particular*, in Futures Studies. At the University of Budapest, *for instance*, you can study topics *like* 'Change and Future' or 'Space and Time in Futures Studies', *to name but two*.

www.CartoonStock.com

'I see your investments going up,
but it's not clear which ones or when.'

NOUNS & PREPOSITIONS

3 Complete the sentences with phrases from the box.

> A growing interest   An increase   A shortage
> Annual consumption   The British taste
> Rapid advances   The developing world's demand

1 _____ for cheap energy is set to grow and grow.

2 _____ for home improvements is reflected in many DIY programmes on TV.

3 _____ in computer technology have changed the way we live.

4 _____ in green issues will lead to more eco-holidays.

5 _____ in road taxes may be the only way to cut exhaust fumes.

6 _____ of bottled water in Italy has reached about 250 litres per person.

7 _____ of fossil fuels will mean we have to find alternative energy sources.

TRANSLATION

4 Translate the quotations into your language.

1 'Everything that can be invented has been invented.' (Charles H Duell, US government official, 1899)

2 'It will be gone by June.' (*Variety* magazine, referring to rock 'n roll, 1955)

3 'Nuclear-powered vacuum cleaners will probably be a reality in ten years.' (Alex Lewyt, president of vacuum cleaner company, 1955)

4 'It's a great invention, but who would want to use it anyway?' (US president, R B Hayes, after a demonstration of a telephone, 1876)

5 'There is no reason anyone would want a computer in their home.' (Ken Olson, computer manufacturer, 1977)

6 'It is apparent to me that the possibilities of the aeroplane, which two or three years ago were thought to hold the solution to the (flying machine) problem, have been exhausted, and that we must turn elsewhere.' (Thomas Edison, American inventor, 1895)

7 'A rocket will never be able to leave the Earth's atmosphere.' (*New York Times*, 1936)

7 | Reading

1 Match the extracts 1–5 to the types of magazine a–e.

a   a food magazine
b   a sports magazine
c   a gardening magazine
d   a gossip and celebrity magazine
e   an interior design magazine

1 of the Rolling Stones. At last year's event in Dordrecht, thousands of fans turned out to line the streets as Her Royal Highness the Princess of

2 defeat for Mourinho. In the press conference after the match, scorer of a hat-trick and captain of the champions this season, Thierry

3 great thing about some of these new hybrids is that they'll stay in flower right through to November if they are regularly watered and taken care of. The brightest colours include a huge scarlet bloom that

4 will be arriving in the shops soon. They have a much more delicate flavour and should be served with a small slice of lemon and a sprinkling of sea salt. A few chopped

5 expert advice, tune in on Wednesday evenings at 9.10 for the latest tips on colour schemes, ways to brighten up your home and, of course, Laurence, with an update on his transformation

2 Look at the photos and headline on the magazine page.

1   What kind of magazine is this from?
2   Which four of the following topics do you think are mentioned?
   a   studies
   b   her family
   c   the people she's worked with
   d   the people she has designed for
   e   her biggest challenge
   f   her plans for the future

3 Read the article to check your answers to exercise 2.

4 Read the article again and answer the questions.

1   What kind of person is Sarah? Underline the words that help you form an impression of her.
2   How many different designers has she worked with?
3   What were the two main challenges that were described in the article?
4   Which do you think was the greatest? Why?

5 Find words or phrases in the article that mean …

1   a student who is getting work experience in a company (paragraph 1)
2   behaviour that deliberately attracts attention (paragraph 1)
3   not afraid to continue doing something difficult (paragraph 1)
4   a large group of people or things that are related in some way (paragraph 2)
5   bringing two contrasting things together (paragraph 2)
6   secret (paragraph 3)
7   behaving in a quiet way without trying to appear better than other people (paragraph 3)

6 Answer the question.

Do you ever read magazines like this? Why or why not?

🔊 READ & LISTEN

7 🔊 **21** Listen to Reading 7 *Sarah Burton – Dressmaker to the stars* on the CD and read the article again.

SARAH BURTON:
Dressmaker to the stars

1 Sarah Burton is no stranger to enormous challenges. When she was still a student at art school studying fashion and design, she was taken on as an intern at the design studios of Alexander McQueen™, one of the biggest names in British fashion. McQueen was synonymous with flamboyance and glamour, his designs worn by some of the most famous, and beautiful, women in the world. His designs were challenging and unconventional and he could be quite demanding of his staff. Intimidated but undaunted, the young Sarah fitted in straight away and joined the company after graduation. She worked closely as a quiet presence at McQueen's side for over fourteen years and took over as creative designer for the company when McQueen died in 2010. Her appointment was no surprise to her colleagues in the fashion industry though many wondered how she would fill the shoes of such a well-known and public figure. Sarah herself said it would be an honour, though a very difficult role to fill.

2 While working alongside McQueen, Sarah had designed outfits for a wide array of famous names, from Lady Gaga to Gwyneth Paltrow, from Cate Blanchett to Michelle Obama. After McQueen's death Sarah had continued to design dramatic, spectacular and unconventional womenswear. But something truly special was required when she was chosen to design the dress for Kate Middleton's wedding to Prince William, the Duke of Cambridge. Marrying the McQueen style with the conventions and expectations of a royal wedding was the challenge of a lifetime.

3 The design of the dress and the designer's identity were kept under wraps right until the last moment, when Kate finally walked up the aisle. The two women had been working on the dress together for

'Kate Middleton marries Prince William.'

months and although there had been press rumours, there had been no confirmation until the day itself. Friends close to the bride said that Sarah had been chosen because of her calm and unassuming presence and because she had a reputation for being open and easy to work with. The final design, with its combination of traditional fabrics (silk and lace) and modern structure won over everybody's hearts. It was, in fact, so successful it has already been copied by thousands of other brides all over the world.

8A | Cold comfort

SYMPTOMS

1 Match the adjectives 1–6 to the nouns a–f to describe symptoms.

1	hacking	a	stomach
2	runny	b	temperature
3	high	c	cough
4	throbbing	d	muscles
5	stiff	e	nose
6	upset	f	headache

2 Match the completed symptoms in exercise 1 to the advice given.

1 Get someone to give you a massage, or take a long, warm bath. _____

2 Suck a mint sweet or drink a glass of milk and honey – that should help the pain. _____

3 Eat boiled rice and fish until you feel better. _____

4 Use very soft tissue or the skin might get sore. _____

5 You may need to use a cool sponge, or take a cool shower to bring it down. _____

6 Take an aspirin and lie down in a dark room until it goes away. _____

3 Put the sentences in the correct order to make three short dialogues.

A: At the chemist's
☐ and if you're not feeling better, see a doctor.
☐ Have you got anything for a sore throat?
☐ Take one of these every four hours for two days

B: At the doctor's
☐ OK, lie down over there and I'll have a look.
☐ What exactly seems to be the problem?
☐ I've been having these terrible pains.

C: Calling in sick
☐ I hope it's nothing serious.
☐ Take it easy and let us know if you're coming in tomorrow.
☐ I'm sorry, I don't think I'm going to make it in today.
☐ I've got an upset stomach and a bit of a temperature.

VOCABULARY FROM THE LESSON

4 Complete the text using an appropriate form of verbs from the box.

be off	come across	
go off	lose take	sound

A: Where's James?

B: He (1) _____ work today. He called earlier and he (2) _____ like death. He said he had a temperature and that he had (3) _____ his food.

A: That's not like James to (4) _____ his appetite. He usually eats like a horse! There must be something wrong with him!

B: So I told him to (5) _____ it easy and give us a call later today. I tried not to (6) _____ as being too anxious, but, well, you know …

A: Yes, I know, we've got that meeting tomorrow and we really need him to be here!

TRANSLATION

5 Translate the jokes into your language.

1 **Patient**: Doctor, Doctor, I think I need glasses.
   Doctor: You certainly do, Sir, this is a fish and chip shop!

2 **Patient**: Doctor, Doctor, I keep getting pains in the eye when I drink coffee.
   Doctor: Have you tried taking the spoon out?

3 **Patient**: Doctor, Doctor, when I press with my finger here … it hurts, and here … and here … What do you think is wrong with me?
   Doctor: You have a broken finger!

WELL WE OBVIOUSLY HAVE TO WAIT FOR THE FULL RESULTS TO COME BACK FROM THE LAB... BUT IF I HAD TO HAZARD A GUESS I'D SUSPECT YOU WERE A BIT UNDER THE WEATHER!

www.CartoonStock.com

8B | Bill of health

HEALTH IDIOMS

1 Rearrange the words to make sentences.

1 weather a feeling she under the bit was .

_____

2 something think I coming down am with I .

_____

3 round definitely going there's bug a .

_____

4 killing back my me was .

_____

5 given bill he clean of was health a .

_____

6 yesterday door I at was death's thought I .

_____

2 Complete the sentences 1–6 in exercise 1 with the phrases a–f.

- [ ] a which was a surprise, considering his lifestyle
- [ ] b but I'm feeling much better today
- [ ] c so I decided to have a massage
- [ ] d so she went to bed
- [ ] e – there are at least five people off work this week
- [ ] f so I'm going to take an aspirin

MODALS OF SPECULATION

3 Find and correct four mistakes in the verbs in italics.

A: Where can she be? She should have been here by now.
B: I don't know. Anything *must have happened* to her.
A: She *can have got* lost.
B: No, I gave her a map.
A: Well, she *may have lost* it.
B: Or she *might be doing* some window shopping, you know what she's like.
C: Yes, but I tried phoning her mobile and she didn't answer.
B: She *mustn't have left* it at home. She's always doing that!
A: Or she *may have let* the battery run down again. That's another of her favourite tricks!
C: Well, there's nothing we can do really, except wait. Hold on, is there another exit to the station?
B: Yes, there is.
C: Well, she *may be waiting* for us there!
B: Yes, of course that *must have been* what she's doing! Let's go and have a look!

4 Delete the one incorrect option for each sentence.

1 It *may have / might have / can't have* been the air-conditioning in the first class carriage. It was freezing!
2 It *mustn't have / must have / could have* been the chicken sandwiches I bought on the train.
3 It *can't have been / might have been / wasn't* the water because I brought it with me from home.
4 I think I *must have / couldn't have / might have* caught it from that man who was opposite me – he was coughing all the time.
5 It *must / can't / might* be contagious. I'd better stay at home.
6 I *may / might / must* have to take a few days off work. I'm not sure yet.
7 It *might be / could be / must have been* on the news – I'd better turn on the TV to see.

5 Look at the photo and complete the sentences.

What happened?
1 He may have _____.
2 He must have _____.
3 He can't have _____.

What's he doing?
4 He might be _____.
5 He can't be _____.
6 He must be _____.

🔘 DICTATION

6 🔘 **22** Write the sentences that you hear.

1 _____.

2 _____.

3 _____.

4 _____.

5 _____.

6 _____.

7 _____.

8c | Alternative therapies

MODALS (PERMISSION, OBLIGATION & PROHIBITION)

1 Choose the best verb forms to complete the text.

There was a time when workers (1) *were allowed to / weren't allowed to* get out of their chairs. They (2) *had to /didn't have to* sit there for up to eight hours a day. They (3) *were allowed to / couldn't* take a ten-minute coffee break, but after that they (4) *had to / didn't need to* ask permission to leave their desks. Now, all that has changed. In modern offices, people (5) *can / must* now leave their work stations without having to ask for permission.

Of course, they still (6) *have to / don't need to* get on with their work, but with wifi connections and cordless phones they (7) *are allowed to / don't have to* be at their desks to be at work. In fact, new office regulations state that workers (8) *mustn't / needn't* sit at their desks for more than 40 minutes at a time, and that they (9) *have to / don't have to* get up and stretch their legs, even if it's just for a few minutes.

2 Complete the text with one word in each gap. Contractions (eg *isn't*) count as one word.

I work as a shop assistant and as part of the job we (1) _____ to wear a uniform. When I first started, I hated the uniform. We (2) _____ to wear a knee-length skirt and tights all year round. We weren't (3) _____ to wear high heels or jewellery, although we (4) _____ allowed to wear earrings, so long as they were small and simple. But things have changed in the ten years I've been working here. We (5) _____ have to wear skirts anymore: we (6) _____ wear trousers if we want, so long as they're smart and clean. But we (7) _____ allowed to wear heavy make-up and any tattoos (8) _____ be covered up.

VOCABULARY FROM THE LESSON

3 Complete the text with phrases from the box.

> colour scheme   ergonomic keyboard
> full spectrum   growing number   low morale
> natural light   work-related illness

Put some light in your life

Spending long hours every day working in artificial light can quickly result in fatigue and (1) _____.

A (2) _____ of companies, as well as schools and colleges, are investing in (3) _____ fluorescent lights which simulate (4) _____.

Change your (5) _____

Therapists advise redecorating your workplace at least once a year. They suggest a combination of calming colours like blue and green to reduce stress.

Look after your back

By far the most common (6) _____ is back pain.

Too many of us sit at our desks for too long. Investing in a good chair and using an (7) _____ can help us develop a better posture.

🔊 DICTATION

4 🔊 **23** Write the sentences that you hear.

1 _____
_____.

2 _____
_____.

3 _____
_____.

4 _____
_____.

5 _____
_____.

8D | Let's dance

CHANGING THE SUBJECT

1 Complete the dialogues with words from the box.

for	reminds	talking	think	saying	way

1

A: I was talking to Bob this morning. He says his mother's out of hospital.

B: Oh, that (1) _____ me, did you get a get-well card for Jean?

A: Oh, sorry, I forgot. I'll get one on the way home from work.

B: No, hold on a second. Come to (2) _____ of it, I may have one in the drawer. I bought one for Robert, but I never sent it! Yes, here it is!

2

A: My dancing hasn't improved despite all the lessons I've had.

B: No, it's got worse, I'm afraid. But (3) _____ of dancing, do you want to go and see *Swan Lake* next month?

A: No. I've had enough of dance. I'm going to give up the lessons and, as (4) _____ *Swan Lake*, I'd prefer to watch a football match.

3

A: So we need to get some food in, tidy up the spare room and, oh, by the (5) _____, I found that book you were looking for.

B: Oh great, thanks, where was it?

A: Under the sofa. Anyway, as I was (6) _____, the spare room needs …

PHRASAL VERBS WITH OBJECTS

2 Replace the verbs in italics with a phrasal verb in the box and make any necessary changes.

bring up	fall for	get back to	look after
make up	put off	run into	sort out

1 You should *take care of* yourself a little more.
2 I'll *contact* you later today with times and prices for the dance classes.
3 I know I should go and see the doctor, but I keep *thinking of something else I have to do instead.*
4 How could you *believe* all his stories?
5 You'll never guess who I *met* at the Apollo last night!
6 Don't *mention* the subject of his health when you speak to him!
7 When they're late, they usually *invent* a story about problems with the bus.
8 Can we *find* a solution to this problem later?

3 Find and correct five mistakes in the sentences.

1 They said they'd get me back to with more information about the dates.
2 I've heard enough of your stories and I won't fall them for any more.
3 It's your problem and you must sort out it.
4 It was my birthday, so they took out me for dinner.
5 Why did you make up it? Why didn't you tell the truth?
6 You never know who you're going to run into when you're in the town centre.

TRANSLATION

4 Translate the dialogue into your language.

A: So, how did you enjoy the ballet last night? It was the first time you've been, wasn't it?

B: Oh, I loved it. It's amazing how they spend so long on the tips of their toes.

A: Yes, they must spend hours and hours training.

B: Yes, they must. But what I don't understand is why they don't just employ taller dancers.

8 | Reading

1 What stories do you know that begin and end with the following words?

'Once upon a …
… lived happily ever after.'

2 Read the story and put the pictures in the correct order.

☐

☐

☐

☐

3 Read the story again and put the events in the correct order.

☐ The man lied to the police.
☐ [1] The man told his wife what he had seen.
☐ The psychiatrist thought the woman was crazy.
☐ The woman contacted the psychiatrist.
☐ The woman refused to believe her husband.
☐ The woman threatened her husband.

4 Find the phrases 1–7 in the story and choose the best definition, a or b. The line numbers are in brackets.

1 a mythical beast (6–7)
  a) an animal that has one horn
  b) an animal that only exists in stories

2 a lily (10)
  a) a flower
  b) a piece of sugar

3 he roused his wife (12)
  a) he shouted at her
  b) he woke her up

4 a gloat in her eye (22–23)
  a) an expression of fear
  b) an expression of happiness

5 a solemn signal (30)
  a) a serious movement with a special meaning
  b) a smile that you cannot control

6 they finally subdued her (32)
  a) they controlled her
  b) they killed her

7 cursing and screaming (37)
  a) shouting in an excited way
  b) using bad language very loudly

5 Who is the crazy person in the story?

🔊 READ & LISTEN

6 🔊 **24** Listen to Reading 8 *The Unicorn in the Garden* on the CD and read the story again.

The Unicorn in the Garden
by James Thurber (1894–1961)

Once upon a sunny morning, a man who sat in a breakfast nook looked up from his scrambled eggs to see a white unicorn with a golden horn quietly cropping the roses in the garden. The man went up to the bedroom where his wife was still asleep and woke her. 'There's a unicorn in the garden,' he said. 'Eating
5 roses.'

She opened one unfriendly eye and looked at him. 'The unicorn is a mythical beast,' she said, and turned her back on him. The man walked slowly downstairs and out into the garden. The unicorn was still there; he was now browsing among the tulips.

10 'Here, unicorn,' said the man and pulled up a lily and gave it to him. The unicorn ate it gravely. With a high heart, because there was a unicorn in his garden, the man went upstairs and roused his wife again. 'The unicorn,' he said, 'ate a lily.' His wife sat up in bed and looked at him, coldly. 'You are a booby,' she said, 'and I am going to have you put in a booby-hatch.'

15 The man, who never liked the words 'booby' and 'booby-hatch,' and who liked them even less on a shining morning when there was a unicorn in the garden, thought for a moment. 'We'll see about that,' he said. He walked over to the door. 'He has a golden horn in the middle of his forehead,' he told her. Then he went back to the garden to watch the unicorn; but the unicorn had gone away.
20 The man sat among the roses and went to sleep.

And as soon as the husband had gone out of the house, the wife got up and dressed as fast as she could. She was very excited and there was a gloat in her eye. She telephoned the police and she telephoned the psychiatrist; she told them to hurry to her house and bring a straitjacket. When the police and the
25 psychiatrist arrived, they sat down in chairs and looked at her with great interest.

'My husband,' she said, 'saw a unicorn this morning.' The police looked at the psychiatrist and the psychiatrist looked at the police. 'He told me it ate a lily,' she said. The psychiatrist looked at the police and the police looked at the psychiatrist. 'He told me it had a golden horn in the middle of its forehead,' she
30 said. At a solemn signal from the psychiatrist, the police leaped from their chairs and seized the wife. They had a hard time subduing her, for she put up a terrific struggle, but they finally subdued her. Just as they got her into the straitjacket, the husband came back into the house.

'Did you tell your wife you saw a unicorn?' asked the police. 'Of course not,' said
35 the husband. 'The unicorn is a mythical beast.' 'That's all I wanted to know,' said the psychiatrist. 'Take her away. I'm sorry, sir, but your wife is as crazy as a jay bird.' So they took her away, cursing and screaming, and shut her up in an institution. The husband lived happily ever after.

Moral: Don't count your boobies
40 until they are hatched.

Glossary

booby *n* a stupid person (*informal, old-fashioned*)
booby-hatch *n* a hospital for the mentally ill (*informal, old-fashioned*)

9A | Celebrity heroes

ADJECTIVE ORDER

1 Insert the adjectives on the right in the correct place in the advertisements 1–8.

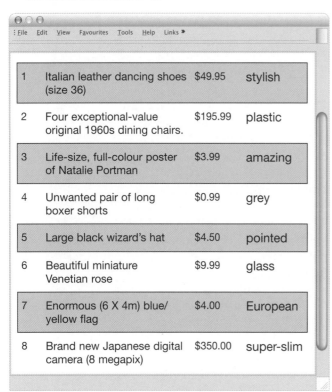

1	Italian leather dancing shoes (size 36)	$49.95	stylish
2	Four exceptional-value original 1960s dining chairs.	$195.99	plastic
3	Life-size, full-colour poster of Natalie Portman	$3.99	amazing
4	Unwanted pair of long boxer shorts	$0.99	grey
5	Large black wizard's hat	$4.50	pointed
6	Beautiful miniature Venetian rose	$9.99	glass
7	Enormous (6 X 4m) blue/yellow flag	$4.00	European
8	Brand new Japanese digital camera (8 megapix)	$350.00	super-slim

2 Complete the descriptions of the pictures with adjectives from the box.

black	French	grey	huge	long	old	round
satin	smelly	square	wooden	woollen		

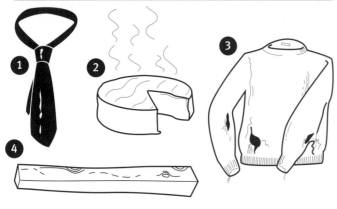

1 a _____, _____, _____ tie

2 a _____, _____, _____ cheese

3 an _____, _____, _____ jumper

4 a _____, _____, _____ stick

VOCABULARY FROM THE LESSON

3 Complete the sentences 1–7 with the phrases a–g.

1 Her work is an *all-consuming* ...
2 I hope you will control your *primitive* ...
3 It was meant as a *harmless* ...
4 Most of my friends are *like-minded* ...
5 She's got a *grotesque* ...
6 There's no need to be *anxious* ...
7 We need to protect *impressionable* ...

- [ ] a about me – I'll be fine.
- [ ] b children who believe everything they hear.
- [ ] c instincts when the meal is served.
- [ ] d joke, so I'm sorry if you were insulted.
- [ ] e passion – she lives and breathes the law.
- [ ] f people who see things the way I do.
- [ ] g poster of a skull and a monster on her wall.

4 Complete the text with prepositions.

Jeremy and I are absolutely obsessed (1) _____ the Eurovision Song Contest and the highlight (2) _____ our year is when all our friends come round and we watch the show together (3) _____ TV. There are usually about 30 (4) _____ us all packed (5) _____ our living room. Jeremy is so devoted (6) _____ the show that he watches all the qualifying competitions on national TV, so it's normal (7) _____ him to be something (8) _____ an expert. Some friends think that our obsession is a cause (9) _____ concern, but I prefer to think (10) _____ it (11) _____ a bit of harmless fun.

🔘 DICTATION

5 🔘 **25** Write the text that you hear.

_____

_____

_____

_____

_____

_____

_____

_____

9B Local hero

ADJECTIVES WITH PREPOSITIONS

1 Match the words in the box to the definitions 1–8.

aware	connected	devoted	familiar
intent	involved	restricted	sympathetic

1 affected by or included in an activity, event or situation _____
2 containing or dealing with one particular thing _____
3 determined to do something _____
4 intended only for people who have been given special permission _____
5 joined to each other or to something else _____
6 knowing about a situation or a fact _____
7 supporting a plan, action, or person _____
8 well-known to you or easily recognized by you _____

2 Complete the sentences with an appropriate preposition.

1 Very few people are aware _____ his true identity.
2 His whole life is devoted _____ the fight against crime.
3 Some of the city's top businessmen are involved _____ criminal activities.
4 The fight is not restricted _____ Gotham City.
5 He is fighting for a world that is free _____ evil.
6 He is also intent _____ getting revenge on the murderers of his parents.
7 He has been responsible _____ the capture of many dangerous criminals.

VOCABULARY FROM THE LESSON

3 Complete the sentences with words from the box.

check out	citizenship	inconvenience
psychologist	reveal	sighting
triumphing	update	

1 We all love a good story of good _____ over evil.
2 We apologize for any _____ you may experience during your stay.
3 We can now _____ the identity of the Caped Crusader.
4 We got Canadian _____ three years after applying.
5 We have just been informed that the police have reported another _____ of a UFO.
6 We turn now to our reporter on the scene for the latest _____ on the war.
7 We will, of course, _____ all the details before printing the story.
8 We've decided to see an educational _____ to ask for advice.

TRANSLATION

4 Translate the text into your language.

Like so many superheroes, Peter Parker's parents were killed during his childhood. Peter was brought up by his uncle and aunt and was a shy adolescent, lacking in confidence and popularity. But then, at the age of fifteen, after being bitten by a radioactive spider, Peter developed superhuman strength and the ability to climb up walls. His career as a crime crusader had begun.

9c | Villains

ADJECTIVES & MODIFYING ADVERBS

1 Complete the table with pairs of adjectives from the box.

> ancient ~~angry~~ awful bad big boiling
> brilliant cold crucial delighted difficult
> enormous exhausted fascinated freezing
> ~~furious~~ good happy hot important
> impossible interested old tired

gradable	ungradable
angry	_furious_
1 _____	_____
2 _____	_____
3 _____	_____
4 _____	_____
5 _____	_____
6 _____	_____
7 _____	_____
8 _____	_____
9 _____	_____
10 _____	_____
11 _____	_____

2 Choose the best words to complete the dialogues.

1 **A:** That was *completely / pretty* scary, wasn't it?
  B: Scary? It was *absolutely / very* terrifying.
2 **A:** That was *really / totally* tiring, wasn't it?
  B: Absolutely. I'm completely *exhausted / tired*.
3 **A:** That was *a bit / absolutely* difficult, wasn't it?
  B: Actually, I thought it was *quite / totally* easy.
4 **A:** That must have been *a little / absolutely* awful for you!
  B: Not really. It was even *completely / slightly* enjoyable at times.
5 **A:** That looks *absolutely / very* similar to your dress.
  B: Not at all. They're totally *different / similar*.
6 **A:** That was *absolutely / a bit* fascinating, wasn't it?
  B: To be honest, I thought it was *totally / very* impossible to understand.

CRIMES

3 Match the words from the box to the newspaper stories 1–6.

> armed robbery   hijacking   kidnapping
> mugging   smuggling   vandalism

1
> An elderly lady in Bexhill-on-Sea turned the tables on two young skinheads who pushed her to the ground and attempted to steal her weekly pension. The woman, a former kung-fu instructor, jumped to her feet, hit …

2
> Glasgow police are interviewing a man in hospital following a failed raid at a bureau de change. Witnesses say that the man, who was wearing a Zorro mask, shot himself in the foot as he demanded money from the cashier.

3
> A man was arrested at Heathrow yesterday when a suitcase full of bottles of whisky fell off his luggage trolley as he was going through customs. A number of the bottles did …

4
> Three teenagers have been ordered to do 120 hours of community service after they were caught spraying graffiti on a train at Wembley station. The three had not noticed a security camera …

5
> Armed police officers rescued a businessman from a disused factory in Perivale yesterday. The man, who had been held in the factory for four hours by a gang demanding one million pounds for his release, telephoned the police on his mobile phone when his captors went out to buy sandwiches.

6
> Passengers and crew on a transatlantic flight on Monday could not control their laughter when a woman stood up, produced a gun from her bag and demanded to be taken to New York. The gun was obviously a plastic toy and the plane was already going to New York.

DICTATION

4 🔊 **26** Write the text that you hear.

_____

_____

_____

_____

_____

_____

_____

9D | Hate list

COMPOUND NOUNS (JOBS)

1 Match the groups of words 1–8 to words from the box to make compound nouns.

> agent   courier   fighter   inspector
> ~~jockey~~   rep   warden   worker

1. champion / disc / top _____jockey_____
2. insurance / intelligence / travel _____
3. fire / jet / street _____
4. bicycle / drug / motorcycle _____
5. factory / office / rescue _____
6. health / school / tax _____
7. student / telesales / union _____
8. park / prison / traffic _____

2 Complete the sentences with a compound noun from exercise 1.

1. Every time I sit on the grass, a _____ comes along and tells me to get up.
2. When I was at university, there was a union and I was a _____.
3. If I were a _____, I'd only play the songs I like.
4. I'd like to be a _____ so that I could get cheap holidays.
5. It must be strange to be a _____ and spend all day looking for dirt.
6. My uncle was in the Air Force and took me up in a _____.
7. I was at the airport once and saw the customs officers stop a _____.
8. The trapped motorists were so relieved when they heard a _____ calling through the fog.

CONTRAST

3 Put the sentences in the correct order.

- [1] For the last ten months, Zaid has been working as a traffic warden, even though
- [ ] graduating as the best student in his year, Zaid finds that employers in his adopted country do not recognize his qualification even though
- [ ] he has had it translated into English.
- [ ] he is a qualified doctor. He took the job, in spite of
- [ ] he receives financial support from his uncle, he has no choice but to work. Despite
- [ ] the low pay, because he couldn't find anything else. Zaid has a family of four to support, and although

VOCABULARY FROM THE LESSON

4 Complete the definitions with words from the box.

> arrogant   cynical   dazzling   evil
> obnoxious   thug   vindictive

1. a _____ man is attractive and fashionable in an exciting way
2. a _____ is someone who behaves in a violent and aggressive way in public
3. someone who is _____ is morally very bad
4. _____ people see the negative side of life and do not expect things to be successful or useful
5. someone who is _____ is cruel to anyone who hurts them and will not forgive them
6. someone who is _____ is very rude, offensive, or unpleasant
7. someone who is _____ thinks they are better or more important than other people and behaves in a way that is rude and too confident

TRANSLATION

5 Translate the sentences into your language.

1. What sort of qualifications do you need to become a nightclub bouncer?

   _____?

2. I think I'll get the job because of my experience as a traffic warden.

   _____.

3. Despite his lack of communicative skills, he made a fortune as an estate agent.

   _____.

4. Let's find out what our survey said about English teachers.

   _____.

5. Although he says he's only doing his job, I think he enjoys handing out parking tickets.

   _____.

6. When some people find out you're a sales rep, they get really obnoxious.

   _____.

9 | Reading

1 How much do you know about Batman™? Choose the correct answers a, b or c.

1 Batman lives in …
   a) Gotham City.
   b) Denver, Colorado.
   c) Metropolis.

2 Batman's enemies include …
   a) the Goodies.
   b) the Joker.
   c) the Teacher.

3 The Batmobile is a special …
   a) bicycle.
   b) car.
   c) mobile phone.

4 Batman's badge is …
   a) pink and black.
   b) white and black.
   c) yellow and black.

5 Batman has a …
   a) dog.
   b) servant.
   c) younger brother called Alfred.

6 Batman changes into his costume in …
   a) telephone boxes.
   b) the men's room.
   c) the Batcave.

7 Batman and Robin are sometimes called …
   a) the Batgirls.
   b) the Dynamic Duo.
   c) the Vampires.

2 Read the article and choose the best title, 1, 2 or 3.

1 The history of Batman and Robin
2 Buying Batman: a collector's guide
3 POW! Batman's universal appeal

3 The sentences a–e were cut from the end of each paragraph of the article. Match the sentences to the paragraphs 1–5.

☐ a

> And the batcave is a cave of wonders, full of strange machines with flashing lights and all kinds of tempting levers and buttons to press and pull.

☐ b

> And so, night after night, he works in the shadows bringing criminals to justice and trying desperately to overcome the trauma that marked his childhood.

☐ c

> But what is the secret of his appeal?

☐ d

> And so long as one kid in the neighbourhood has got the newest bat present, everyone else is going to want one, too.

☐ e

> These are the same people who spend millions of pounds collecting Batman memorabilia: first issue comic books, limited issue toys and all sorts of gadgets.

4 Read the article again. In which paragraph(s) 1–5 can you find the information a–h?

☐ a Selling Batman toys and costumes to children is very profitable.
☐ b A lot of superheroes disappeared after the 1950s.
☐ c The original Batman only came out at night.
☐ d A lot of Batman merchandise is targeted at an adult audience.
☐ e Not all Batman merchandise is original.
☐ f Very young children like Batman, too.
☐ g Batman appeals to both adults and children.
☐ h Batman shows human weaknesses.

5 Match the verb phrases in bold in the text to one of the words or phrases 1–6.

1 full of   4 go to in large numbers
2 possess   5 appeared in public
3 has a lot of   6 find

6 Why does Batman appeal more to boys than to girls?

🔊 READ & LISTEN

7 🔊 **27** Listen to Reading 9 Batman on the CD and read the article again.

Batman

Like all good heroes, Batman is not perfect. He is eaten up by revenge: revenge for the deaths of his own parents and for those of the 'boy wonder', Robin. He and Robin manage to capture Antonio Zucco, the gangland boss who was responsible for the deaths of Robin's parents, but Batman will never be able to **track down** the criminal who killed his own parents in cold blood.

He hides his obsession behind a mask and **is plagued by** doubts. Who is he? Which is his true identity? Is he the philanthropist millionaire Bruce Wayne or the masked vigilante working in the shadows? Bruce Wayne spends his days putting his money to work to help the poor and needy, but at night he takes the law into his own hands and sometimes comes very close to crossing the thin line between crime and crime fighting. This is the Batman that appeals to the adult readers of the DC comics and the adult audiences that **flock to** the cinemas to see the Batman films.

But there's another Batman, too. One who works by day, whose punches and kicks are accompanied by cartoon 'POWs' and 'KERPLUNKs'. The Batman of the cult 1960s TV series, shown all over the world and appealing to an adult sense of humour, as well as to the superhero fantasies of much younger viewers. To these younger kids he's just one of them, with an envious choice of great toys to play with: batmobiles, batbikes, bathelicopters, batboats, batjets, you name it – he's got one.

Batman™ first appeared in May 1939. He was one of a host of superheroes who were fighting to bring peace to the streets of American cities. But, unlike most of the hundreds of costumed crime fighters that **took to the streets** between the 1930s and 1950s, Batman survived well into the 21st century and he is now possibly the world's most popular superhero. He is certainly number one in the field of superhero merchandising. There are more than 1,000 bat-items licensed for sale in the US, and probably just as many cheap imitations. You can buy all sorts of things, from dolls and costumes to clocks, perfume and inflatable beds.

What three-year-old wouldn't want to **get their hands on** all those goodies? The Batman merchandising machine has known how to make the most of this very lucrative market and Batman's appeal has grown and grown and grown. Bat toys and costumes are available for kids as young as three years old and parks and playgrounds across the world are **peopled with** miniature batpeople.

Batman memorabilia

'I like Batman 'cos he fights crime and his ears stick up' (Sam, aged 3)

10A | Good deeds

REFLEXIVE VERBS

1 Replace the words in italics with phrases from the box.

> adapt yourself to   expressed yourself
> content yourself   distinguish yourself
> ask yourself   you should consider yourself

1 *I think you were* lucky – it could have been much worse.
2 *Think about* what would be better: to lose or not to have tried at all.
3 You need to learn to *cope with* new situations or you'll end up having a nervous breakdown!
4 Congratulations, I think you *put your ideas into words* really well.
5 If you can't change a situation, then the best thing is to learn to *be happy* with it.
6 If you want to *be successful* as an artist, you're going to have to work much harder.

2 Add the reflexive pronoun *themselves* to the text where necessary (seven times).

It is natural that parents endanger in order to protect their young, both in the human and animal world. But this decision to sacrifice for their children is not always the best choice. How will the children survive without their parents if they are too young to look after? Parents need to remind that they need to look after their own safety first, so that they are then in a better position to look after that of their children. This is also true in day-to-day life. Parents who dedicate not only to their children, but also to their other interests and passions, make better parents. They should not consider to be the slaves of their children, but rather pride on being happy, satisfied individuals who share their love of life with their family.

VOCABULARY FROM THE LESSON

3 Complete the questions with prepositions from the box.

> against   for   from (x2)   to (x2)

1 What exactly is it that **sets us apart** _____ the beasts?
2 Do you **attach great importance** _____ material goods?
3 Are you willing to **sacrifice yourself** _____ a good cause?
4 Will they ever be able **to provide an answer** _____ the question?
5 Would you ever consider **giving evidence** _____ your best friend?
6 Do you think you would **benefit** _____ a holiday?

4 Complete the sentences with the expressions in bold and a preposition in exercise 3. Make any necessary changes.

1 I think this room would really _____ a complete makeover.
2 My grandparents _____ their independence and never like asking for help.
3 The ability to control our tempers is another thing that _____ primitive man.
4 The jury listened attentively as she _____ her ex-husband.
5 There's no need for you to _____ your job. The company would never do the same for you.
6 We believe we can _____ your problem.

TRANSLATION

5 Translate the proverbs into your language.

1 Actions speak louder than words.
2 Saying is one thing, and doing, another.
3 A good deed is never lost.
4 Easier said than done.
5 One good deed deserves another.
6 The evil that men do lives after them.
7 It is not how long, but how well we live our lives.

10B | Giving

REPORTING

1 Rearrange the words in italics to complete the sentences.

1 She asked him *wanted the jacket to keep if he him for her*

_____.

2 He said *he'd later back for it afternoon come that* _____.

3 They told us *charity giving they to it were*

_____.

4 We asked them *they'd coming be back day next the whether* _____.

5 He told them *couple days of he away for a going might be* _____.

6 She asked him *thought when getting back he he'd be* _____.

7 He said *finished with want it it he'd and didn't anymore* _____.

2 Change the sentences in exercise 1 into direct speech.

3 Find and correct six mistakes in the text.

I asked him where was his new jacket and why wasn't he wearing it. He said it had been stolen from his office. I asked him why hadn't he told me and he said he doesn't want to upset me. When I told him I had known the truth, he said was he really sorry, he hadn't liked the jacket from the start, but he didn't know how to tell me.

4 Complete the report of the dialogue.

1 'We found your jacket.'
2 'Did you know about the money in the pocket?'
3 'I was going to use it to pay a builder.'
4 'Have you got the money with you?'
5 'How much money did you leave in the pocket?'
6 'There should be two thousand pounds in twenty-pound notes.'
7 'Why did you throw the jacket away?'
8 'I didn't throw it away; it was my ex girlfriend who threw it away.'

She told him that (1) _____ and she asked him (2) _____. He said (3) _____ and he asked (4) _____. She asked him (5) _____. He told her (6) _____ and she asked him (7) _____. He explained that (8) _____.

'I'm not asking you, Mister, I'm telling you!'

COLLOCATIONS WITH *GIVE*

5 Complete the sentences with words from the box.

| consideration | lecture | permission | priority |
| piece of my mind | problems | speech | warning |

1 I'll give it top _____ and do it right away.

2 We won't decide now, but we'll give your idea some _____.

3 This car's been giving us _____ for ages now. I think we should get rid of it.

4 I'm feeling really nervous – I've got to give a _____ at the dinner.

5 He refused to give _____ to film on his premises.

6 His father gave him a _____ about the importance of studying hard.

7 People get into trouble there every year, even though they're given plenty of _____ about the dangerous currents.

8 He really shouldn't have done that. I'm going to give him a _____!

● DICTATION

6 ● **28** Write the text that you hear.

_____

_____

_____

_____

_____

10c | Aid worker

JOB RESPONSIBILITIES

1 Complete the words with vowels to form verbs often used in job descriptions.

1 p r _ m _ t _   5 c _ _ r d _ n _ t _
2 l _ _ _ s _   6 t r _ c k
3 _ v _ r s _ _   7 s _ _ k _ _ t
4 p _ r t _ c _ p _ t _ 8 f _ c _ l _ t _ t _

2 Replace the words in italics with a verb in exercise 1.

1 I was asked to *take part* in an international aid conference.
2 I had to *act as a messenger* between the headquarters and the grass roots workers.
3 I often need to *check and sometimes correct* the writing of promotional materials.
4 One of my responsibilities is to *look for* new volunteers.
5 We attempt to *help local groups to overcome problems with* decision making.
6 A key part of my job is to *attract people's attention to* local events and projects.
7 Someone needs to *organize* the work of the various departments and volunteers so that they work efficiently together.
8 We *follow* the progress of all new projects very closely in the first year.

REPORTING VERBS & PATTERNS

3 Report the direct speech with the verbs given.

1 'We don't want to have anything to do with the project.'
They refused _____.
2 'We're thinking of visiting your site in the North.'
He mentioned _____.
3 'I really don't know much about recent developments.'
She admitted _____.
4 'You really must come and see our new offices.'
They invited us _____.
5 'I'll pass the information on as quickly as possible.'
He promised _____.
6 'The company has no connection whatsoever with the local authorities.'
They denied _____.
7 'I really think you should try again.'
She encouraged me _____.
8 'Don't travel through the mountains after dark.'
They warned them _____.

4 Find and correct four mistakes in the text.

> After lengthy talks with our delegates, the local education authority has agreed opening four new schools in the area. We have managed to persuade them putting forward 50% of the funding and we have suggested to spend this money on the school buildings. In return the education authorities have asked us supplying the teaching staff and materials.

DICTATION

5 🔘 **29** Write the text that you hear.

_____
_____
_____
_____
_____
_____
_____

10D | A good job

JOB INTERVIEWS

1 Complete the texts with one word in each gap.

1 I know I have a tendency (a) _____ take on too much work and I need to learn to delegate more.

2 I've been working (b) _____ the voluntary sector (c) _____ the last five years. To start (d) _____, I worked (e) _____ a volunteer at a charity shop and then gradually worked up to being regional manager.

3 I think this job would give me the chance (f) _____ develop my interpersonal skills.

4 I'm usually good (g) _____ motivating staff and I take pride (h) _____ my ability (i) _____ initiate and manage change and innovation.

5 Mainly my experience in similar projects. I've worked (j) _____ various projects where I've been successful in implementing structural changes.

2 Match the questions a–e to the responses 1–5 in exercise 1.

☐ a Can you tell us something about your work experience to date?
☐ b Why are you interested in the post?
☐ c What do you think you can bring to this job?
☐ d What do you see as your strengths?
☐ e And what about your weaknesses?

VOCABULARY FROM THE LESSON

3 Complete the dialogues with an appropriate form of verbs from the box.

attend	develop	give	meet	set	write

1 **A:** How's the new job going?
  B: Fine, a bit stressful, there are so many deadlines to (a) _____. And they're all impossible!

2 **A:** I'm going to New York at the weekend.
  B: Wow! Really?
  A: Yeah, I'm (b) _____ a conference.
  B: Are you (c) _____ a talk?
  A: No! Thank goodness!

3 **A:** I had a chat with my boss today.
  B: And?
  A: She says I've got to learn to be more organized, (d) _____ priorities, that kind of thing.

4 **A:** How come you're so late?
  B: We had to (e) _____ a last-minute press release.
  A: Oh yeah, what had happened?

5 **A:** So are you really going to take the job, then?
  B: Yeah, I know it isn't a great job, but at least I'll get a chance to (f) _____ my computer skills.

TRANSLATION

4 Translate the text into your language.

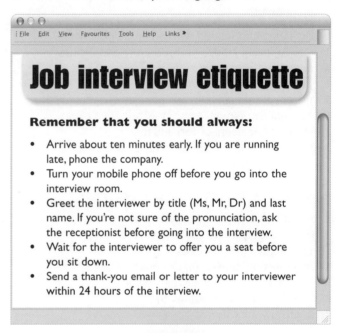

Job interview etiquette

Remember that you should always:

- Arrive about ten minutes early. If you are running late, phone the company.
- Turn your mobile phone off before you go into the interview room.
- Greet the interviewer by title (Ms, Mr, Dr) and last name. If you're not sure of the pronunciation, ask the receptionist before going into the interview.
- Wait for the interviewer to offer you a seat before you sit down.
- Send a thank-you email or letter to your interviewer within 24 hours of the interview.

www.CartoonStock.com

'Number four wasn't too bad – at least he removed his personal CD earphones for most of the interview.'

10 | Reading

1 Put the lines in the correct order.

☐ Peace Prize for its fight against torture.
☐ the death penalty. It has over two million
☐ Amnesty International campaigns for
☐ human rights and the end of torture and
☐ members and was awarded the Nobel

2 Look at the extracts 1–6 from the website. Match them to the hyperlinks A–F on the main web page.

3 Look at the extracts 1–6 again. Which of the following ways of supporting Amnesty are mentioned?

1 exchange information with other people online
2 join Amnesty groups on Facebook™ and Twitter™
3 organize a sponsored cycle ride
4 put on events with a local group
5 recycle old things to make money
6 sign online petitions
7 speak to Members of Parliament
8 work with other students to raise awareness of Amnesty issues

4 Explain the phrases 1–7 in your own words.

1 standing up for human rights (extract 1)
2 death sentences are commuted (extract 1)
3 like-minded people (extract 2)
4 making a big impact on campus (extract 3)
5 makes a lasting contribution (extract 3)
6 taking joint action (extract 5)
7 a gift in your will (extract 6)

🎧 READ & LISTEN

5 🎧 **30** Listen to Reading 10 *Amnesty* on the CD and read the website extracts again.

1 **Amnesty International is a movement of ordinary people from around the world standing up for humanity and human rights.**

And we're a movement that produces extraordinary results. Prisoners of conscience are released. Death sentences are commuted. Torturers are brought to justice. Governments are persuaded to change their laws and practices.

Our achievements have a huge impact on the lives of individual people. And your support makes us even stronger.

2 Local groups are vital to the work of Amnesty. Whether you're an old hand at grass roots campaigning, or you've never done anything like this at all, you'll enjoy meeting like-minded people and really making a difference.

Groups usually meet once a month and with more than 285 local groups across the UK, you are sure to find one that suits you.

By joining your local group you could be involved in letter writing, raising awareness about human rights in your local area, organizing events and stalls, lobbying MPs and MEPs, getting Amnesty into your local media as well as campaigning activities like Greenwich and Blackheath's Embassy Crawl, below.

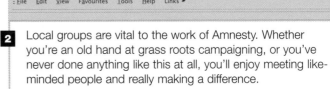

- ■ Download a list of all groups (pdf)
- ■ Find out more about local group campaigning and download resources
- ■ Find out about Regional Representatives
- ■ Read about our Featured Group of the month

3 **Student activists play a vital role in Amnesty's campaigns** – they are often our most active members, showing an amazing amount of creativity and enthusiasm in all they do, and making a big impact on campus and in their wider community. Amnesty students' commitment and hard work is highly valued and celebrated by the movement.

The Student Action Network campaigns are co-ordinated through regular communications, events, information and support. There are **over 100 groups** in the network, and each stands up for human rights and makes a lasting contribution to the work of Amnesty in their own way.

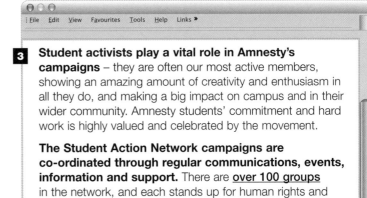

4

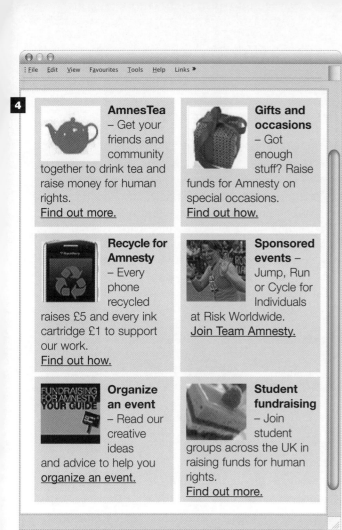

AmnesTea – Get your friends and community together to drink tea and raise money for human rights.
Find out more.

Gifts and occasions – Got enough stuff? Raise funds for Amnesty on special occasions.
Find out how.

Recycle for Amnesty – Every phone recycled raises £5 and every ink cartridge £1 to support our work.
Find out how.

Sponsored events – Jump, Run or Cycle for Individuals at Risk Worldwide.
Join Team Amnesty.

Organize an event – Read our creative ideas and advice to help you organize an event.

Student fundraising – Join student groups across the UK in raising funds for human rights.
Find out more.

5

Amnesty's specialist e-networks put their interests and professional skills to work. The e-networks campaign on their professional or personal interests, and by sharing information and taking joint action, they create far more pressure than would be possible working alone. When you **sign up**, you will receive regular emails with news, updates and campaigning actions. You can also stay informed by visiting your network's homepage.

6

If you would like to help Amnesty's work to protect human rights, you can give money in a variety of ways. Select from the options below for the way that suits you best:

- Donate now
- Join us now and become a member of Amnesty
- Open an Amnesty saver account
- Leave a gift in your will
- Give in memory
- Company giving
- Personal loans
- Ethical investments
- Wedding list giving
- Give at an event

11A | Globe-trotting

GEOGRAPHICAL FEATURES

1 Match words from the box to their dictionary definitions 1–8.

> bay   canal   cape   desert   falls
> ocean   peninsula   strait

1 a long piece of land mostly surrounded by water _____
2 one of the large areas of salt water that cover most of the Earth _____
3 an artificial river _____
4 a large area of land that continues further out into the sea than the land it is part of _____
5 a place where water flows over the edge of a cliff, rock or other steep place _____
6 an area of the coast where the land curves inwards _____
7 a large area of land with few plants and little water and where the weather is always dry _____
8 a narrow area of water that joins two larger areas of water _____

2 Match the descriptions to six of the words from the box in exercise 1.

1 It took us eight days to cross it from East to West. The heat during the day was almost unbearable.

2 We heard it before we saw it, an incredible thundering noise – and there it was in front of us. An amazing sight.

3 There's a great viewpoint on the Spanish side, just west of Gibraltar. The mountains of Morocco look so close across the strip of sea separating Africa from Europe.

4 We climbed over the top of the hill and there it was in front of us. Almost a perfect semicircle with a tiny white-washed fishing village right at the water's edge.

5 The boats lined up, ready to go through the first of five locks which would take us up 40m to the next stretch of water.

6 We sat on the beach and watched the sun go down as the waves lapped gently against the rocks.

THE & GEOGRAPHICAL NAMES

3 Find and delete five unnecessary uses of *the* in the text.

> The Straits of Magellan are named after the Portuguese explorer who first sailed through this narrow passage connecting the Atlantic and the Pacific. The Straits lead from the border between the Chile and the Argentina in the East, past the town of the Punta Arenas to the islands of the Queen Adelaide Archipelago in the West. It was the only safe route between the two oceans until 1914 when the Panama Canal was opened, enabling ships to sail right through the Central America. It was a popular route with prospectors trying to reach the coast of the California in the 1849 Gold Rush.

4 Add *the* in the gaps where necessary.

The cruise was incredible. Out of this world. We set off from the town of (1) _____ Ushaia, the world's southernmost city in the foothills of (2) _____ Andes. Then we sailed through (3) _____ Drake Passage out into (4) _____ Antarctic ocean, turning our backs on (5) _____ South America. We were heading for (6) _____ South Shetland Islands at the tip of (7) _____ Antarctic peninsula, an amazing strip of ice with the most spectacular glaciers practically falling into the sea. And there were lots of penguins, too!

💿 DICTATION

5 💿 **31** Write the sentences that you hear.

1 _____.
2 _____.
3 _____
_____.
4 _____
_____.
5 _____.

11B | South is up

BINOMIALS

1 There are mistakes in four of the phrases in italics in the sentences. Find and correct them.

1 The golden rule of public speaking is always to keep it *sweet and short*. _____

2 He worked *long and hard* to get to where he is today. _____

3 His study is an amazing place: it's full of *pieces and bits* from all over the world. _____

4 It's always better to put things down in *white and black* so you've got a record of the decisions taken. _____

5 He was *born and bred* in Scotland, but spends most of his time on the French Riviera. _____

6 Try not to get too angry and remember it's always better to *forget and forgive*. _____

2 Complete the texts with words from the box.

blood	choose	flesh	fro	here
now	pick	tested	to	tried

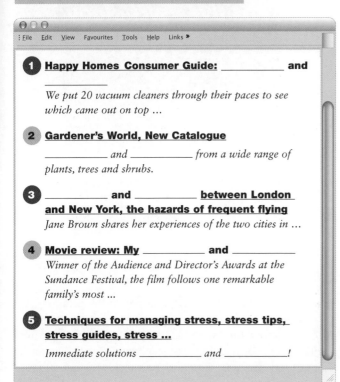

1 **Happy Homes Consumer Guide:** _____ **and** _____

We put 20 vacuum cleaners through their paces to see which came out on top …

2 **Gardener's World, New Catalogue**
_____ *and* _____ *from a wide range of plants, trees and shrubs.*

3 _____ **and** _____ **between London and New York, the hazards of frequent flying**
Jane Brown shares her experiences of the two cities in …

4 **Movie review: My** _____ **and** _____
Winner of the Audience and Director's Awards at the Sundance Festival, the film follows one remarkable family's most …

5 **Techniques for managing stress, stress tips, stress guides, stress …**
Immediate solutions _____ *and* _____!

VAGUE LANGUAGE

3 Shorten the text by deleting all the vague language.

It's kind of difficult to say exactly what it is to be Australian. People talk about national identity and stuff like that, but it's really much more personal. It's stuff like the things you do every day, your family, your friends and so on, and the things you do together. The way we live our lives sort of defines who we are, and I suppose there is a lifestyle which could be called more or less typically Australian. It's a simple lifestyle, an outdoor lifestyle. It doesn't mean we're all sports mad, surfing or kayaking or something all day long, but it does mean that we tend to spend a lot of time outside, you know, in our gardens, on the beach, taking it easy.

4 Add words from the box to the text.

know	like	of (x 2)	on	or (x 2)	so

I've loved maps since I was a kid. I suppose they kind remind me of my dad. He had a huge one in his study. It covered the whole wall. It must have been like five metres long something. We used to spend hours just, you, looking at the map and planning imaginary journeys and stuff that. We used to stick flags in it to show where we'd been on holiday and so. And since I left home I've always, more less, had a map in my room. And my bookshelves are packed with them, road maps, street maps, atlases, globes and on. Some people say I'm obsessed and I guess they're sort right.

TRANSLATION

5 Translate the text into your language.

My favourite place is a small fishing village in Cornwall. I first went there when I was ten years old or so. We used to go there on family holidays, more or less every summer. It was a great place for kids with rockpools and hidden beaches and all that kind of stuff. But I still love it as an adult. Now I'm more into the surf and the seafood restaurants and that kind of thing, you know, adult stuff.

ARTICLES

1 Choose the correct options to complete the text.

What makes you happy?
Our readers answered (1) *a / the* question.

Jean: Spending some time on my own, listening to (2) **the / –** music, reading (3) **a / the** magazine, or simply sitting on (4) **the / –** sofa!

Roy: When (5) **a / the** kids come to visit, seeing them play in (6) **a / the** garden, watching them as they run and shout … and (7) **the / –** wonderful silence in (8) **an / the** house when they've gone home!

Nick: Going for (9) **a / the** jog in (10) **the / –** park after (11) **a / –** work, drinking (12) **a / the** cup of (13) **the / –** tea as I read my newspaper.

Kay: (14) **The / –** travelling, visiting (15) **the / –** new places, meeting (16) **the / –** new people and looking at (17) **a / the** photos when (18) **a / the** holiday's over!

2 Find and delete seven unnecessary articles in the text.

What is happiness? The secret's in the 'flow'.

Researchers believe that happiness, or 'a life satisfaction' occurs most frequently when people lose themselves in the daily activities. The term used to describe this is 'flow'. A people in flow may be doing something very simple, sewing a button on a shirt or cooking a meal. They may be involved in a work, playing a musical instrument, taking part in the sport or losing themselves in a good book. The result is always the same.

The important thing is to identify the activities in your a day-to-day life that absorb you most and to build your life around these things. That, it seems, is the secret of the true happiness.

VOCABULARY FROM THE LESSON

3 Replace one or two words in each sentence with a word from the box.

affluent	correlation	crucial
euphoric	perceptions	tackle

1 Very often other people's opinions of us are much more important than our bank balance.
2 There is no simple, straightforward relationship between happiness and money.
3 It is very important to take a number of different factors into account.
4 It is also important to remember that we are looking at overall happiness and not single extremely happy moments.
5 But having measured happiness levels, we still need to deal with the basic problem of finding ways of making people happier.
6 The really wealthy people in society are not necessarily the happiest.

TRANSLATION

4 Translate the text into your language.

Today, it is claimed, is the happiest day of the year. Researchers claim that a combination of good weather, the proximity of the summer holidays, long light evenings and plenty of outdoor activities are responsible for the nation's happiest day this year. Earlier this year they claimed that January 23 was the most depressing day of the year, with the Christmas holidays almost forgotten, the long-awaited January payslip still a week away and dark, cold nights keeping everybody indoors.

11D | Perfect locations

DESCRIBING LANDSCAPE

1 Complete the texts with words from the box.

cliffs   estuary   gorge   hills   peaks   valleys

The closing scene shows our heroine running barefoot across a wide sandy (1) _____.

The gentle, rolling (2) _____ and fertile, wooded (3) _____ are a perfect backdrop for this adaptation of the famous Shakespeare comedy.

The main action takes place inside a deep, narrow (4) _____, hidden from the outside world, where the time travellers come face-to-face with a range of prehistoric animals.

The jagged, snowy (5) _____ and the tall, steep (6) _____ of the Rocky Mountains are as much the stars of this action movie as the actors themselves.

SO & SUCH

2 Choose the correct words to complete the text.

Have you ever wondered how sci-fi movie makers create (1) *so / such* incredible new worlds? Read on and find out. It's not (2) *so / such* difficult; all you have to do is look around you – and be prepared to travel!

Star Wars® is set in 'a galaxy far, far away', but you too can visit the faraway planets that have become (3) *so / such* famous on the big screen. Luke Skywalker's home, Tatouine, which looks (4) *so / such* strange, (5) *so / such* much like it's on another planet, is based on a village in Tunisia.

Matmata is (6) *so / such* a beautiful spot that it was already popular with tourists and Luke's home in the film is actually a hotel.

3 Rewrite the sentences with the words in brackets.

1 It's been a long time since I've seen a really good film. (*such*)
2 The scenery was incredibly beautiful, it was almost a distraction from the film. (*so … that*)
3 The story is very simple. (*such*)
4 But the acting is extremely good and it really brings the story alive (*so … that*)
5 The closing scene was one of the saddest I've ever seen, it made me cry. (*so*)
6 It's a truly excellent movie and I highly recommend it. (*such*)

⊙ DICTATION

4 ⊙ **32** Write the dialogue that you hear.

A: _____?

B: _____.

A: _____?

B: _____.

A: _____.

B: _____.

11 | Reading

1 Read the article and put the paragraphs A–D in the correct order in the table.

PARA	1	2	3	4	5	6
	■					■

2 Read the article again. In which paragraphs 1–6 can you find the information a–h?

a   It is possible for everyone to be happier.

b   People are happier when they feel that they belong to a group.

c   People's happiness was evaluated a number of times during the experiment.

d   Slough is often considered to be an unattractive place to live.

e   Some activities took place in the countryside near Slough.

f   The aim of the experiment was to find out if happiness could be increased in the town.

g   The experts had not expected the experiment to work so well.

h   The volunteers worked with artists and musicians for a performance at the end of the project.

3 Find the words and expressions 1–7 in the article and choose the correct definition, a or b. The line numbers are in brackets.

1   dull (08)
  a) boring
  b) interesting

2   soaring (16)
  a) decreasing very quickly
  b) increasing very quickly

3   resounding (19)
  a) complete
  b) incomplete

4   turn around (27)
  a) start being successful
  b) stop being successful

5   literally (32)
  a) an exaggeration of the number
  b) the exact number

6   commune (49)
  a) communicate with words
  b) communicate without words

7   over the course of (56)
  a) after
  b) during

4 Look at the information on a web search engine. On which of the websites could you find more information about the experiment described in the article?

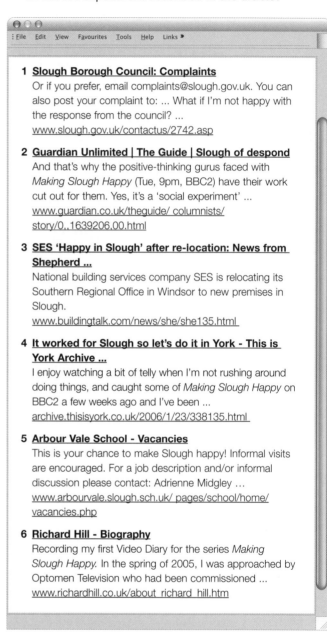

File   Edit   View   Favourites   Tools   Help   Links ➤

1 Slough Borough Council: Complaints
Or if you prefer, email complaints@slough.gov.uk. You can also post your complaint to: ... What if I'm not happy with the response from the council? ...
www.slough.gov.uk/contactus/2742.asp

2 Guardian Unlimited | The Guide | Slough of despond
And that's why the positive-thinking gurus faced with *Making Slough Happy* (Tue, 9pm, BBC2) have their work cut out for them. Yes, it's a 'social experiment' ...
www.guardian.co.uk/theguide/ columnists/story/0,,1639206,00.html

3 SES 'Happy in Slough' after re-location: News from Shepherd ...
National building services company SES is relocating its Southern Regional Office in Windsor to new premises in Slough.
www.buildingtalk.com/news/she/she135.html

4 It worked for Slough so let's do it in York - This is York Archive ...
I enjoy watching a bit of telly when I'm not rushing around doing things, and caught some of *Making Slough Happy* on BBC2 a few weeks ago and I've been ...
archive.thisisyork.co.uk/2006/1/23/338135.html

5 Arbour Vale School - Vacancies
This is your chance to make Slough happy! Informal visits are encouraged. For a job description and/or informal discussion please contact: Adrienne Midgley ...
www.arbourvale.slough.sch.uk/ pages/school/home/vacancies.php

6 Richard Hill - Biography
Recording my first Video Diary for the series *Making Slough Happy*. In the spring of 2005, I was approached by Optomen Television who had been commissioned ...
www.richardhill.co.uk/about_richard_hill.htm

5 Do you think a similar experiment would work in your town? Why or why not?

💿 READ & LISTEN

6 💿 **33** Listen to Reading 11 *Making Slough Happy* on the CD and read the article again.

Making *Slough* Happy

1

Slough is a modern commuter town, 20 miles west of London, and although it is really no different from any other satellite town on the commuter routes to London, it has gained an unfortunate reputation for
5   being both ugly and boring. The name, which means a muddy field, certainly doesn't help, nor does its portrayal in the TV comedy show, *The Office*, where it was shown as being dull and depressing. And it was no surprise when a questionnaire showed that
10 the levels of happiness in Slough were well below the national average.

A ☐

As the experiment drew to a close the final questionnaires were distributed. The experts were surprised and delighted by the results. The overall
15 happiness ratings of the group had increased by more than 30%, soaring way above the national UK average. If Slough were a country, it would be the happiest country in the world! The experiment had been a resounding success.

B ☐

20 So last summer, a team of happiness experts arrived in town. Their aim was to conduct a social experiment, to see if they could make the people of Slough happier. The science of happiness claims that anyone, no matter how happy they are already, can
25 become happier by adopting a few small lifestyle changes and developing a more positive attitude. The team had three months to turn the town around and their work was filmed for a BBC documentary.

C ☐

Towards the end of the three months, they all came
30 together to stage a Grand Finale. A group of the volunteers, helped and supported by artist Helen Marshall, took literally thousands of photos of day-to-day life in Slough and put them together to create an enormous collage of a happy, smiling face.
35 Another group trained to sing an anthem that had been written specifically for the occasion. And a number of local youth groups (a Caribbean drumming band and an Indian dance group, amongst others) joined them on the day of the Grand Finale to stage
40 a free karaoke concert in the middle of Slough town centre.

D ☐

They chose 50 volunteers to help them with their experiment. The volunteers took part in a series of activities and events and their levels of happiness
45 were measured at regular intervals. The activities included camping overnight in nearby woods, dancing in the aisles of a local supermarket and learning to sing. The volunteers experienced the power of saying thank you, of smiling at strangers and of taking time
50 out to commune with nature. They experimented with laughter therapy and learnt to enjoy housework.

6

But what exactly had the experiment shown? That if we sing as we work and smile at strangers, the world will be a happier place? Possibly. But the real
55 success of the experiment had much more to do with the sense of community and purpose that developed over the course of the project than any of the individual activities. The experiment was a success because the people who took part in it felt they were
60 doing something important. They felt valued and useful. This is the key to real happiness.

12A | Loot

PASSIVES REVIEW

1 Choose the best verb forms to complete the text.

Most valuable natural pearl necklace
A single-strand pearl necklace which (1) *reputedly wore / was reputedly worn* by French queen Marie-Antoinette (2) *auctioned / was auctioned* for €910,313 ($1,476,345) at Christie's, Geneva, Switzerland, on 16 November 1999. It (3) *was / was been* the highest price that (4) *had ever paid / had ever been paid* for a natural pearl necklace. It (5) *consists / is consisted* of 41 large pearls and it (6) *held / is held* together by a diamond cluster clasp. The necklace (7) *once owned / was once owned* by Woolworth heiress Barbara Hutton (US). It (8) *bought / was bought* by an anonymous European buyer.

2 Complete the text with the past simple or present perfect passive forms of the verbs in brackets.

File   Edit   View   Favourites   Tools   Help   Links ➤

8 THINGS YOU DIDN'T KNOW ABOUT
Treasure Island

1 More than 50 movie versions _____ (*make*) of the book.

2 It _____ (*first publish*) in instalments in a children's magazine.

3 It _____ (*adapt*) for both TV and the stage.

4 The first three chapters _____ (*write*) in three days.

5 They _____ (*then read*) aloud to his family, who made suggestions for improvements.

6 It _____ (*translate*) into over 25 languages.

7 The author, Stevenson, _____ (*pay*) 100 pounds for the book.

8 It seems that treasure maps with an X showing the treasure _____ (*never use*) by pirates.

VOCABULARY FROM THE LESSON

3 Complete the text with verbs and phrasal verbs from the box.

carry out	head for	make off with
raid	threaten	track down

Modern day pirates
Pirates still exist today, and although they don't (1) _____ coastal towns anymore or (2) _____ buried treasure, they continue to attack passing ships and (3) _____ as much loot as possible. Modern-day pirates use small boats which are often disguised as fishing boats, and they often (4) _____ their raids against large cargo ships, which have to slow down as they (5) _____ narrow channels such as the Suez Canal or the Straits of Malacca. They board the ships, (6) _____ the crew with violence and grab the contents of the ship's safe. Sometimes the pirates take over the ship and sail it to a nearby port, where it is repainted and given a new identity.

DICTATION

4 🔊 **34** Write the sentences that you hear.

1 _____
  _____.

2 _____
  _____.

3 _____
  _____.

4 _____
  _____.

Google Earth
For Pirates

12B | Bounty hunter

IDIOMS (MONEY)

1 Insert six missing words into the story.

From rags to riches

Seven years ago Jayne Bingley didn't have a penny her name. She was living from hand mouth and struggling to pay the rent at the end of the month. Now she lives in the lap luxury and has money burn. It all began when a friend introduced her to eBay™. She began with 20 dollars and some bits of old furniture. Now her antiques company is making millions and she's worth fortune. 'It's a gold mine,' she said. 'I started out the red and eBay was like a miracle cure. If you've got something to sell, there's always somebody out there who's ready to buy it.'

PASSIVE REPORTING STRUCTURES

2 Rearrange the words in italics in the correct order.

1 Butch Cassidy and the Sundance Kid *been known have to are* two of the most successful bank robbers in the West. _____

2 *that it been rumoured has* they met in prison where they were both serving sentences for horse theft. _____

3 After a particularly daring robbery on a mining company *crossed they have to reported were* the border into Mexico. _____

4 However, *now is that it believed* they escaped to Argentina. _____

5 *that thought is it* they bought a ranch in Patagonia and started life afresh as honest cowboys. _____

6 But then a nearby bank was robbed by two masked men *to said were have who spoken* in English. _____

7 Bounty hunters tracked down and shot two outlaws *be were to believed who* Butch and Sundance in a small town in Bolivia. _____

3 Replace the words in italics with a passive reporting structure. Begin with the word in brackets.

1 *Many reports state that* the Sundance Kid never shot or killed anyone. (*it*)

_____

2 *There were rumours that* they were often accompanied by a woman. (*it*)

_____

3 She went by the name of Etta Place, though *many people believe this was a false name.* (*this*)

_____

4 *A lot of people said that they were* very polite and gentlemanly. (*they*)

_____

5 In Argentina, *there were rumours that they were* in trouble with the law. (*they*)

_____

6 *Some people have suggested that* they returned to a life of crime because they were bored. (*it*)

_____

TRANSLATION

4 Translate the text into your language.

Millions of items are bought and sold on eBay™ every day. Anything can be sold as long as it is not illegal. One of the biggest things that has ever been sold on the site was a World War II submarine. It was put up for auction by a small town in New England. A few tablespoons of water that had reportedly been left in a plastic cup after Elvis Presley had taken a drink from it were sold for $455.

12c | Scam

PHRASAL VERBS 2

1 Put the lines in the correct order.

☐ **away** information like passwords or bank details. They use the details to apply for credit, shop online and generally **rip you**

☐ **up** all kinds of excuses in order to persuade you to **give**

☐ **away**. So why aren't we equally careful with our email? Millions of people have **fallen**

☐ **off**. And nine times out of ten the scammers **get away**

☐ **back** your money.

☑ If a suspicious salesperson came to your door, you'd have no hesitation in **turning them**

☐ **for** bogus emails supposedly sent by banks or online shopping sites. The emails **make**

☐ **with it**. It is virtually impossible to get them to **hand**

2 Complete the sentences using an appropriate form of the phrasal verbs in bold in exercise 1.

1 They were _____ because they were not appropriately dressed.

2 The forgery was so good that literally thousands of people _____ it.

3 The thieves were forced to _____ the stolen goods.

4 The taxi driver _____ me _____, charging me twice the normal fare.

5 He _____ a story about how he had to get up early for work the next day.

6 Don't _____ your special access code to anyone outside the company.

CAUSATIVE

3 Complete the text with *to* + infinitive or the past participle form of the verbs in brackets.

File   Edit   View   Favourites   Tools   Help   Links ➤

Feeling lazy?

Get someone else (1) _____ (*do*) it for you – whatever it is! In today's service society, there's very little we have to do for ourselves any more. We can have our house (2) _____ (*clean*) by a cleaning service; we can have all our meals (3) _____ (*cook*) and (4) _____ (*deliver*) by a variety of different restaurants. We can get the hairdresser (5) _____ (*come*) to our home to style our hair and we can even ask a masseur to pop in to the office so we can have our feet (6) _____ (*massage*) as we work. We can get a personal shopper (7) _____ (*do*) all our shopping for us and have it all (8) _____ (*bring*) to our front doors. And if we've got enough money, why not get a personal style consultant (9) _____ (*decide*) what we're going to wear every day?

🔊 DICTATION

4 🔊 **35** Write the sentences that you hear.

1 _____.

2 _____.

3 _____.

4 _____.

12D | Dollar bill

GENERALIZING

1 Correct the mistakes in the sentences.

1 People worry more about money than their health, general speaking.
2 In the whole, pensioners are much better at keeping within their budgets than young people.
3 People carry less cash on them, on general, than they did ten years ago.
4 As the rule, supermarket shoppers prefer to pay by credit card than in cash.
5 For a most part, shops and restaurants are happy to accept all major credit cards.
6 People only use cash for minor purchases by or large, such as a cup of coffee, a newspaper or a bus ticket.

US & UK ENGLISH

2 Complete the crossword.

ACROSS
2 where you throw your rubbish if you live in the US (7, 3)
5 the quickest way to get around in London (11)
6 where pedestrians walk along the side of roads in American towns and cities (8)
11 a large purple vegetable which is used in Mediterranean dishes (9)
12 if you're in the US and you need some water, you could try turning this on (6)

DOWN
1 this is where you go to refuel your car in the UK (6, 7)
3 if you're in the US, they've got long legs; if you're in the UK, you wear them under your trousers (5)
4 you wear this over your shirt in the US (4)
5 one way of getting to the other side of an American street (9)
7 see 5 down – this is what you'd use in the UK (6)
8 the UK version of 4 down (9)
9 this is what you would ask for at the end of your meal in a New York restaurant (5)
10 a game played with eleven players and a round ball (6)

3 Complete the dialogues with some of the words in the crossword in exercise 2.

1 **A:** Where's your dustbin?

   B: Sorry? Oh you mean, the _____! It's under the sink.

2 **A:** What's today's special?

   B: Eggplant with sun-dried tomatoes.

   A: Eggplant? What's that?

   B: Oh, sorry, I think you call it _____.

3 **A:** Did you see the football on TV last night?

   B: Football? There wasn't any on last night.

   A: Sorry – I should have said _____.

4 **A:** Excuse me. I'm having problems with the _____ in our bathroom.

   B: I'm sorry, I don't understand.

   A: I can't seem to turn the hot water on.

5 **A:** Could we have the bill, please?

   B: Certainly, I'll bring you your _____ right away.

6 **A:** Hey, I love your new _____!

   B: What do you mean? Oh, you like my trousers – thanks!

TRANSLATION

4 Translate the dialogue into your language.

Lord Fermor: Young people, nowadays, imagine that money is everything.
Lord Henry: Yes, and when they grow older they know it. But I don't want money. It is only people who pay their bills who want that, and I never pay mine.

(Oscar Wilde, *The Portrait of Dorian Gray*)

12 | Reading

1 Translate the words in bold in the dictionary extract into your language.

> **curse** /'kɜːs/ verb ★
>   **2** [T often passive] to use magic powers to make bad things happen to someone
> **curse** /'kɜːs/ noun
>   **2** [C] a bad situation or event caused by someone's deliberate use of their magic powers: *the curse of the Pharaohs* – **put a curse on sb/sth** *He was sure someone had put a curse on his house.*
>   **2a** the words used for causing bad luck – opposite BLESSING
> **cursed** /'kɜːst/ adj **1** affected in a negative way by a magic curse: *They were starting to believe that the house was cursed.*

2 Read the article on page 75 and choose the best summary.

1 Scientists have still not found an explanation of the Pharaoh's curse.
2 The curse on Lord Caernarvon's family continues to this day.
3 The Pharaoh's curse is an entertaining story.

3 Read the article again and choose the best answer, a, b, c or d.

1 Why did Lord Caernarvon think that his dreams had come true?
   a) Because he had his own race horses.
   b) Because he had recovered from his car crash.
   c) Because he thought that Carter had discovered treasure.
   d) Because he was the owner of the gold of Tutankhamun.

2 What was special about Carter's discovery?
   a) It was the world's greatest archaeological discovery.
   b) The burial chamber was hidden behind a secret door.
   c) The Pharaoh's burial mask was wet.
   d) Tutankhamun was a boy-king.

3 Who encouraged people to believe in the curse of the Pharaoh?
   a) Egyptian archaeologists
   b) Howard Carter
   c) popular newspapers
   d) Sir Arthur Conan Doyle

4 What happened to most of the people who went into the tomb?
   a) Nothing special.
   b) They breathed the mushroom spore.
   c) They died of mysterious illnesses.
   d) They lived in fear for the rest of their lives.

5 What does the writer think is the truth about Caernarvon's death?
   a) He was cursed by the Pharaoh.
   b) His death was caused by an insect.
   c) His murder will never be explained.
   d) Supernatural forces were probably responsible.

4 Match the words and phrases in the text 1–7 to the definitions a–g. The line numbers are in brackets.

1 was dripping with (26)
2 had come to an untimely end (59–60)
3 had struck lucky (27–28)
4 desecrated (41)
5 dried up (65)
6 sparked the legend (68–69)
7 leave a lot to the imagination (86)

☐ a died before their time
☐ b do not provide all the necessary details
☐ c slowed down and stopped
☐ d spoiled a religious place
☐ e was covered in
☐ f was at the beginning of all the stories
☐ g were very fortunate

🔊 READ & LISTEN

5 🔊 **36** Listen to Reading 12 *The Pharaoh's Curse* on the CD and read the article again.

The PHARAOH'S Curse

1 When George Herbert received a telegram telling him to come to Egypt immediately, he thought his dreams had come true. Herbert, better known as Lord Caernarvon, was a rich aristocrat, an owner of racehorses
5 and a racing-car enthusiast. He was also a keen Egyptologist and for fifteen years he had been sponsoring the work of Howard Carter, an archaeologist who was searching for treasure in Egypt's Valley of the Kings. Carter had made an amazing discovery but would go no further without his
10 sponsor. Archaeological work stopped until Caernarvon arrived in Cairo two weeks later. After four more days of digging, a door was uncovered in a tomb that belonged to the Pharaoh Tutankhamun. Carter was so excited that he spent the night at the tomb before he finally entered
15 Tutankhamun's resting place the next day. With a candle in his hand, Carter said nothing for two or three minutes until the impatient Caernarvon asked him if he could see anything. 'Yes,' replied Carter, 'it is wonderful.'

2 The treasure that was spread out before them was the
20 greatest that has ever been found. The burial chambers were stuffed with weapons, clothes, furniture and chariots, which took ten years to be catalogued. The body of Tutankhamun himself was found inside two coffins made of solid gold and the Pharaoh's
25 burial mask, also of solid gold, was dripping with jewels. Carter and Caernarvon had struck lucky. But just five weeks after the opening
30 of the tomb, Caernarvon became the first victim of the curse of the Pharaoh.

3 Doctors could not
35 identify the mysterious illness that brought Caernarvon's life to a close. It was reported that mysterious forces had
40 been released after Carter desecrated the tomb. The popular press jumped on the story and captured the public's imagination. One
45 reporter claimed that a text near the entrance to the tomb read 'I will kill all who pass this door'. It was also reported that the lights in
50 Cairo had gone out at the moment of Caernarvon's death. Within ten years, six more people who had been present at the opening of the tomb had come to an
60 untimely end. Where would the curse of the Pharaoh strike next?

Carter opens the tomb

4 Sir Arthur Conan Doyle, creator of Sherlock Holmes, was convinced that the Pharaoh's tomb contained a deadly mushroom spore and that more deaths would follow. But
65 surprisingly, the number of victims dried up. Later studies showed that the average age of death of those who had gone into the tomb was relatively low. Many of Carter's team lived well into old age, and the death that sparked the legend of the curse turned out to be not so mysterious
70 after all. In actual fact, Caernarvon, who had never fully recovered his health following a car crash, was killed by a mosquito bite which became infected. This, remember, was at a time before antibiotics, and the power supply in Cairo was very irregular.

5 But the curse of the Pharaoh and the tales of walking mummies continue to live today. Despite substantial evidence to the contrary, it seems that there are many people who are ready to believe that dark, supernatural forces are behind the deaths of Caernarvon and others.
80 Could it have been the work of an evil spirit? Or was it radiation from radioactive rocks in the tomb? Had the ancient Egyptians made contact with alien visitors and developed sophisticated technology? Was Tutankhamun himself the victim of a cold-blooded murder? The theories
85 are fun, but they leave a lot to the imagination, and, sadly, are only the stuff of Hollywood.

Writing for Upper Intermediate students

You may be wondering why we've included more writing at this level of *Straightforward*. The reason for this is because writing often becomes so much more important at Upper Intermediate level – when you may need to write English for school project work, for business or to take examinations.

Writing is often challenging in another language and we can sometimes feel more pressure. It's important to get it right – if we *say* something wrong in another language people forget it quickly, but when we write, people can be less forgiving and, as it's recorded in print, they may read it again and again!

In order for you to become a good writer of English, it's important to remember a few golden rules:

- Don't hurry – give yourself lots of time. Always plan your writing before you start. It can be helpful to read the question you need to answer and then go away and 'chew it over' during the day. This may help to make your ideas clear.
- Sit down and plan the structure of your writing. The structure will make it easier for the reader to follow your thoughts and enjoy your writing. Try to think of something original to say about the topic so that your reader is interested and motivated to read more.
- When you begin writing, don't make your sentences too long. In some languages it's considered good style to use very long and grammatically complex sentences. This is not usually the case in English.
- Try to use basic words less at Upper Intermediate level. For example, instead of *and*, try to use words and expressions such as *moreover* and *as well as*; instead of *but*, use *however* and *despite*.
- Remember to use common phrases traditionally used for different types of writing. See page 77 to help you with this. This will make your writing more sophisticated and natural.
- Always leave time to check your written work. If you feel a bit unsure about it, why not do one section early and show it to your teacher? It might be helpful to get some feedback before you write the whole composition.
- Finally, enjoy writing! It's fun to write and it can become just as much fun in another language, once you've understood the conventions of that language.

WORKBOOK WRITING LESSONS

There are six writing units in this Workbook. Each unit consists of two pages (A & B) which practise and build on the writing lessons in the Student's Book.

Page A provides **additional practice of the language focus points** presented in the Student's Book. Use these pages alongside the Student's Book writing lessons.

Page B provides **a structured writing 'lesson', building up to a writing task**. These pages tie in with the topics of the even numbered units in the Student's Book. Sample answers for these writing tasks are provided in the answer key (pages i–xvi).

Student's Book unit		Workbook unit
Unit 1	A job application	1A Applying for a job (1)
Unit 2		1B Applying for a job (2)
Unit 3	A composition	2A Writing a composition (1)
Unit 4		2B Writing a composition (2)
Unit 5	A review	3A Writing a review (1)
Unit 6		3B Writing a review (2)
Unit 7	An email to a friend	4A Writing to a friend (1)
Unit 8		4B Writing to a friend (2)
Unit 9	A story	5A Writing a story (1)
Unit 10		5B Writing a story (2)
Unit 11	A report	6A Writing a report (1)
Unit 12		6B Writing a report (2)

Useful language to improve your writing

NARRATIVE LANGUAGE

At first …
At the beginning …
Initially …
At the beginning …
After a while …
Later on …
Afterwards …
Subsequently …
Eventually …
In the end …
Finally …

WRITING A COVERING LETTER

I am writing in response/reply to your advertisement.
I understand you are currently looking for …
I would like to apply for the position of …
I am interested in gaining experience in …
I have enclosed/attached my CV and the names of two referees.
I am available for interview/to begin work at your convenience.
Please do not hesitate to contact me if you require further information.
I look forward to hearing from you.
Thank you for your time and consideration.

EXPRESSING AN OPINION

It could be argued that …
It is fair to say that …
It is generally recognized …
It is reasonable to say …
It seems to me …
Many people feel …
Most people would agree …
There is no doubt that …

DESCRIBING A FILM/TV SHOW/SERIES

The show/film is named after/based on …
The series/film centres on …
It follows the lives of …
It tells the story of …/It paints a very accurate picture of …
The star of the show/film is …/It stars …
The role of … is played by …
His performance is worthy of an Oscar®/Emmy.
What I liked most/least about it was …
Critics praise it for …

INFORMAL GREETINGS (EMAILS, NOTES, POSTCARDS)

Hi/Hello! How are you doing?
Thanks for your email/letter.
Sorry I haven't written for ages/so long.
It's/was great to hear from you!
Sorry I missed your call.
This is just a quick note to say …
Speak to you later.
Bye for now. Speak soon.
All the best and love to the family.
Say hi to everyone from me.
Love from everybody here.
Keep in touch.

INVITATIONS

Informal

Do you feel like going out tonight?
How about coming with us?
Do you fancy doing something later?
What about coming round to my place?
Would you like to come with us?
We were wondering if you'd like to come with us.

Formal

It gives us great pleasure to invite you to …
We would be delighted/pleased if you could join us.
Mr & Mrs X request the pleasure of your company at …

WRITING A REPORT

Introduction

The purpose of this report is to …
The report will discuss/analyse/describe …
The following report examines/reviews/considers …
The report is divided into three parts.

Conclusion/recommendations

I would like to suggest/recommend that …
Taking everything into consideration …
On balance, I think that …
To sum up, I suggest we …
In conclusion, my own view is that …

WRITING THE MINUTES FOR A MEETING

Here is a summary of the decisions taken and the action agreed on …
X opened the meeting by …
It was agreed that …
After some discussion, it was eventually decided that …
X has agreed to/volunteered to …
Y presented the results/the options …
The next meeting will be held on …

1A | WRITING Applying for a job (1)

LANGUAGE FOCUS

1 Find and underline ten unnecessary capital letters in the CV extracts.

1

> I translated over 2,000 Recipes from Spanish to English for a web-based recipe book, *La Cocina Española*. The Job involved liaising with my co-writer, Jane Goode and the Editors responsible for the Project.

2

> I am a highly motivated and enthusiastic Graphic Design Student. I am looking for an initial placement in a dynamic work environment.

3

> rock-climbing: I was an active member of the outdoor pursuit club at School and have been interested in Rock Climbing ever since.

2 Match the extracts 1–3 in exercise 1 to one of the CV sections.

Personal profile
Education
Work experience
Skills
Interests
References

3 Choose the correct spelling, a, b or c.

1   a) profesional   b) professional   c) proffessional
2   a) personal   b) personel   c) personnal
3   a) knowlege   b) knowlegde   c) knowledge
4   a) essential   b) esential   c) essentiel
5   a) expereince   b) experiense   c) experience
6   a) sucessful   b) successful   c) succesful
7   a) volontary   b) voluntery   c) voluntary
8   a) responsibilities   b) responsabilities
    c) responsibilitys
9   a) referrees   b) referres   c) referees

4 Complete the text with the correctly-spelt words in exercise 3.

> A (1) _____ CV will include information about your work (2) _____, your (3) _____ qualifications and your (4) _____ qualities. Remember to include all relevant jobs, including (5) _____ work and add a short description of the duties and (6) _____ involved. It is also (7) _____ that you include information about your (8) _____ of languages and computing skills. Last, but not least, remember to include the names and contact details of two (9) _____.

5 Complete the sentences 1–6 with the phrases a–f.

1   I **am experienced** …
2   I particularly enjoy **helping** …
3   My **duties** …
4   **I am looking** …
5   I **was an active** …
6   I worked as a volunteer **at** …

☐ a   **member of** the university's film society. _____
☐ b   **included** liaising between parents and school authorities. _____
☐ c   **in** restaurant work and outside catering. _____
☐ d   **other people with their work.** _____
☐ e   **first** and was then given a job as a part-time guide. _____
☐ f   **for** a job in the retail industry. _____

6 Match the sentences in exercise 5 to the jobs from the box.

> chef   film critic   museum curator
> personal assistant   shop assistant   teacher

7 Replace the phrases in bold in exercise 5 with one of the expressions 1–6.

1   took an active part in
2   job involved
3   have experience of
4   supporting the work of others
5   initially
6   my aim is to find

1B | WRITING Applying for a job (2)

READING

1 Look at the cover letter and answer these questions.

1 What kind of job is Mark looking for?
2 Has he done this kind of job before?

> Dear Mr Wright,
>
> I understand from an article on your website that you are looking for volunteers to help out at the animal rescue shelter in Newham. I am writing to enquire whether you have any vacancies for the months of June and July, as I will be staying with friends in the area during that period. I am currently studying journalism at Cardiff University and I am looking for an opportunity to work in the voluntary sector with a view to publishing an article about my experience.
>
> Although I have not worked at an animal shelter before, I am an animal lover. I have had experience of looking after a variety of pets and farmyard animals, including dogs, cats, horses, sheep and goats. I am familiar with your organization and greatly admire the work you do. I would really like to help in whatever way I can. If I could be of use in your Press Department, this would be a welcome bonus.
>
> I have included a copy of my CV. I will try to contact you within the week to arrange an interview. Thank you for your time and consideration.
>
> Yours sincerely,
>
> Mark Goodsworth

2 Look at the cover letter again and decide if these statements are true (T) or false (F). Correct the false sentences.

1 Mark is writing in response to a job advert. ___

2 He has never worked for an animal shelter. ___

3 He is looking for a job for the summer holidays. ___

4 He doesn't know much about the organization. ___

5 He's going to call or write again in a few days' time. ___

6 He's going to send a copy of his CV by post. ___

LANGUAGE FOCUS

1 Complete the phrases 1–8 with the phrases a–h.

1 I am writing to ...
2 I am looking for ...
3 I am currently ...
4 I have included ...
5 I will try to contact you within the week to ...
6 Thank you for ...
7 I am familiar with your organization and ...
8 I have had experience of ...

☐ a an opportunity to work in the voluntary sector.
☐ b arrange an interview.
☐ c enquire whether you have any vacancies for July.
☐ d greatly admire the work you do.
☐ e looking after a variety of pets and animals.
☐ f studying journalism at Cardiff University.
☐ g your time and consideration.
☐ h a copy of my CV.

2 Match sentences in exercise 1 to the points a–f in the notes.

> **How to write a cover letter**
> Whether you are answering a job advert or sending your CV to a potential employer you should always write an accompanying cover letter. The letter should include the following points:
> **Paragraph 1**
> a Introduce yourself
> b Explain your reason for writing
> **Paragraph 2**
> c Describe your experience
> d Explain why you are interested in the organization
> **Paragraph 3**
> e Promise to follow up on your application
> f Thank the reader for considering your application

WRITING

1 Choose one of the organizations below. Write a cover letter enquiring about the possibility of work during the next holidays. Remember to follow the advice given in Language focus exercise 2.

> **SUMMER WORK**
> Join the crew of the *Sea Heaven* on its annual summer cruise around the Pacific. Many positions available: bar, restaurant, activities organizer, cleaning, baby-sitting service, etc.
> **Good rates of pay.**
> Send CV to Heaven Cruises, P.O. Box 666, Grand Cayman

> **HOTEL STAFFING SOLUTIONS INC**
> We are currently looking for staff to fill temporary positions in hotels in five continents. Vacancies for all types of work.
> *Free training, flights and insurance. Tax free.*
> Fax CV and cover letter NOW to: HSS Inc + 371 22 060606 (ref. XP8)

LANGUAGE FOCUS

1 Put the paragraphs in the correct order.

☐ _____ Skirt-like garments are worn by men all over the world, either as part of their national dress or as an everyday alternative to trousers. The Greeks and Albanians wear the *fustanella* – a pleated white skirt – as part of their traditional costume. Many men in Southern India wear *dhotis* – checked cotton sarongs – both for work and leisure. In the Himalayan Kingdom of Bhutan all men wear a knee-length robe called a *gho*.

☐ _____ The Irish have their own version of the kilt, too, as do the Welsh, and many Celtic émigrés wear kilts as a symbol of their heritage. Kilts are also fast becoming a fashion item. Celebrities (footballers, pop singers, film stars) are increasingly being photographed in variations on the traditional kilt. A Seattle-based company has launched the *utilikilt*, a modern take on the traditional kilt, designed for day-to-day use.

☐ _____ Kilt historians suggest that the kilt may have originated in Norway and was subsequently introduced to Scotland by the Vikings. Whatever the truth of its origins, there is no doubt that a man in a kilt is synonymous with Scottishness. Although more than 80% of Scotsmen do not actually own a kilt, most will, at some time, hire one for a formal occasion, be it for weddings, football matches or to attend the Highland Games.

2 Insert the topic sentences a–c at the beginning of the paragraphs in exercise 1.

a Kilts are not exclusive to Scotland – there are kilts from other countries, too.
b The kilt is probably the most well-known symbol of Scotland.
c Kilts are not the only alternative to trousers for men.

3 Complete the sentences with phrases from the box.

complete without	favourite icons
not the only	of which less than
synonymous with	the best known of

☐ 1 The double-decker bus is _____ London.
☐ 2 Cuddly koala bears are another of Australia's _____.
☐ 3 Kangaroos are probably _____ all Australian animals.
☐ 4 No image of London transport is _____ the inclusion of a black cab.
☐ 5 The large red bus is _____ form of transport associated with the capital city.
☐ 6 Australia is an enormous country, _____ 10% is inhabited.

4 Match the topic sentences 1–6 in exercise 3 to the composition titles, a or b. Then order the sentences 1–6, as they would appear in the composition.

a Images of the Capital _____
b Australian wildlife _____

5 Choose the correct word to complete the sentences.

1 It could be *argued / agree* that it has some of the most beautiful beaches in the world.
2 It is fair to *say / doubt* that it has never been famous for its food.
3 It is *general / generally* recognized that it produces the finest wines in the region.
4 It is *reasonable / reasonably* to say that it is one of the world's richest countries.
5 It *seems / feels* to me that it is often misrepresented in the world press.
6 Many people *seem / feel* that its image needs updating.
7 Most people would *argued / agree* that it is a great holiday destination.
8 There is no *say / doubt* that its historic importance is greatly undervalued.

6 Which of the sentences in exercise 5 are true for your country?

2B | WRITING A composition (2)

READING

1 Read the composition and put the paragraphs in the correct order.

☐ He began stealing cattle to provide for his family and, before long, he and his gang were on the run. They robbed banks and shared the money with friends and family. In no time, Ned had gained himself a reputation as an Australian Robin Hood.

Ned Kelly: an Australian hero

☐ But after the gang killed three police officers in a shoot out, he also gained a reputation as a police killer. He and his gang were finally captured in Glenrowan, a small town in Victoria. Three gang members were killed. Ned was arrested and charged with murder. He was hanged in 1880 at 25 years of age.

☐ The outlaw, Ned Kelly, is one of Australia's greatest folk heroes. But he is also a source of great debate. Was he a working-class hero, or a criminal who robbed and killed?

☐ A year later, an enquiry into the Glenrowan siege resulted in the dismissal of several police officers. The town of Glenrowan has become synonymous with the Kelly legend and, every ten years, a re-enactment is held of the gang's historic last stand.

☐ From a young age, Ned was in trouble with the law. At the age of sixteen, he was wrongfully imprisoned for stealing a horse and from then on, he was convinced that the police were persecuting him and his family.

2 Read the composition again and put the events in the correct order.

☐ Ned was hanged.
☐ Police officers lost their jobs.
☐ The Kelly gang started robbing banks.
☐ Ned was accused of stealing a horse. *(marked 1)*
☐ Three policemen were killed.
☐ Glenrowan became famous.

LANGUAGE FOCUS

1 Complete the text with time expressions from the box.

| at 38 years of age | At the age of eleven | before long |
| Eleven years later | from a young age | From then on |

PHOOLAN DEVI

A Phoolan Devi, otherwise known as the Bandit Queen, fought for the rights of low-caste women in India, first as the leader of a gang of bandits and later as a Member of Parliament.

B Phoolan, born into a poor fishing family, rebelled against her fate (1) _____. (2) _____ she was sold into marriage, but she stood up to her husband's abuse and was thrown out of his house. It is thought that she was then kidnapped by a gang of bandits and (3) _____ she had become one of them. When a group of upper-caste villagers killed her bandit lover, Phoolan formed her own gang. (4) _____, she took revenge on the landowners who made life so difficult for the poor villagers.

C For ten years she led raids to save child brides from early marriages and stole from the upper caste landowners. She eventually surrendered to the police and was sent to prison. (5) _____ she was released and stood for Parliament. There, she continued her fight for women's rights until, (6) _____, she was shot and killed outside her home in New Delhi.

2 Look at the text in exercise 1 and complete the paragraph summaries with words from the box.

| early | famous | grew | how |
| summary | why | brief | |

A a (1) _____ explanation of (2) _____ the person is (3) _____

B a (4) _____ of the person's (5) _____ life

C a description of (6) _____ the legend (7) _____

WRITING

1 Use the paragraph summaries in Language focus exercise 2 to write a composition about a hero from your country.

3A | WRITING A review (1)

LANGUAGE FOCUS

1 Complete the review with the correct prepositions.

> This classic TV mini series was first released
> (1) _____ 1996, but it is still a top ten favourite.
> This is arguably the best screen adaptation (2) _____
> Jane Austen's much-loved novel. Colin Firth, in the role
> (3) _____ Darcy, is masterful. The chemistry
> between him and Elizabeth Bennet (played (4) _____
> Jennifer Ehle) really brings the story to life. The action
> is set (5) _____ a series of beautiful stately homes,
> the cast are dressed (6) _____ meticulous period
> costume, and the choreography and music all add up to a
> truly great experience.

2 Complete the review with the missing words.

The film (1) a_____ of *Bridget Jones's Diary* is a total success. It tells the (2) s_____ of Helen Fielding's best-selling novel of the same name and manages to convey the same sense of humour and romance as the original. Renée Zellweger is totally (3) c_____ as paranoid 30-something Bridget, and the role of Mark Darcy is played to (4) p_____ by Colin Firth. Personally, I think his performance is (5) w_____ of an Oscar®! And anyone who saw *Pride and Prejudice* (the TV mini-series that (6) s_____ Colin Firth as the original Mr Darcy) is sure to agree.

3 Complete the text with phrases from the box.

> in the lead role   It tells the story   Its plot is
> Most of the action   which featured
> The best moment in the whole movie
> The cast has no stars   the part

> *Attack of the Killer Tomatoes* has been called one of
> the cheapest and worst science fiction movies of all
> time. (1) _____ of a group of scientists who save
> the world from the threat of mutant tomatoes that
> have turned violent. (2) _____ is an accidental
> helicopter crash, but this unfortunate pilot error
> obviously ate up the entire budget for special effects.
> (3) _____ clearly takes place in a studio and
> the killer tomatoes are less than frightening when
> you can see their wheels. (4) _____ and their
> involvement in *Killer Tomatoes* did not help their
> careers. David Miller looks uncomfortable
> (5) _____ and you have to wonder why he
> accepted (6) _____. Ten years after the film's
> release, a sequel, *Return of the Killer Tomatoes,*
> (7) _____ a young George Clooney, was made.
> (8) _____ basically the same as the original.

4 Look at the pictures. Write a short description of the plot of *Attack of the Killer Tomatoes* using the present simple.

3B | WRITING A review (2)

READING

1 Read the review of a TV series and decide whether it is mainly positive or negative.

The West Wing

*T*he *West Wing*, a TV drama series which centres on the White House, is one of the most popular TV shows in the US. It is watched by more than fifteen million viewers each week and it has won a record number of Emmy awards.

The show follows the life of fictional Democrat president, Jed Bartlet, and his team, during their eight years in office. Jed Bartlet (played by Martin Sheen) is undoubtedly the star of the show. The president's role was fairly unimportant in the first few shows but audience reactions soon prompted the programme makers to bring him centre-stage.

The show is named after the West Wing of the White House, the location of the president's Oval Office and the offices of his senior staff. Real-life politicians follow the show closely and say it paints a very accurate picture of how the US government actually works. Educationalists praise the show, saying that it helps people understand the complex workings of government, while TV critics praise it for the quality of its dialogue and story lines.

2 Read the review again. Put the topics in the order in which they are mentioned.

- ☐ the main character
- ☐ the name
- ☐ what people say about it
- ☐ the setting
- ☐ the story and the characters
- ☐ the number of people who watch it

LANGUAGE FOCUS

1 Complete the review with the phrases a–f.

a The show is named
b The series centres
c it follows
d it paints a very accurate picture
e the star of the show is
f TV critics praise it

The Office must be the number one TV comedy series ever! (1) _____ on a paper company in Slough and (2) _____ the day-to-day lives of the office workers in the style of a documentary. (3) _____ after the location of all the scenes – the various offices and meetings rooms of the paper company.

There is no doubt that (4) _____ David Brent, played by comic genius Ricky Gervais. His performance is magnificent, as are those of all the cast. Office workers around the world will all agree that (5) _____ of the world of office politics, and (6) _____ for its hilarious dialogue and perfect timing.

2 Complete the phrases a–f in exercise 1 so that they are true for a TV series you know.

WRITING

1 Write a review of a popular series on TV in your country. Remember to include information about the setting, the storyline and the characters and to explain why it is so popular.

LANGUAGE FOCUS

1 Put the lines in the correct order for an email message.

☐ We really must get together and catch up sometime soon.

☐ Maybe we can meet up then.

☐ Lots of love, T.

☐ I'm sorry I was out when you phoned.

☐ I can't believe it's been three months since we last spoke. So much has happened!

☐ Speak to you later today,

☐ I'll phone you later today when I know the dates for sure.

☐ I'm coming down to London next week for a business meeting.

☐ Right, got to go now, the boss is looking over my shoulder!

[1] Hi Jane, thanks for your message.

2 Compete the sentences with words from the box.

again	call	doing	last
nice	now	quick	too

1 Hello, how are you _____?

2 Thanks for your email. It was so _____ to hear from you!

3 Just a _____ note to say we had a really good time last night.

4 OK. 8 o'clock suits me, _____.

5 Anyway, sorry _____ I can't come. I hope you have a great time!

6 I'll _____ you at the weekend to see how things are going.

7 One _____ thing. Can you get some bread in on the way home? Thx!

8 Bye for _____. Speak soon.

3 Rearrange the words in italics to make invitations.

1 *fancy you going do* to the cinema tonight? That new French film's on. _____

2 Hi, *invite you writing to I'm to* a surprise party for Debby's 30th birthday. _____

3 Mr and Mrs Bob Carl *company of pleasure your the request* at their daughter's graduation ceremony. _____

4 Sorry, I can't make the party tonight. *to place coming what round my about* tomorrow for something to eat? _____

5 We're going to the beach for the weekend. *if wondering we like were would you to* come with us. _____

6 *us be pleased you could join we very would if* to celebrate the launch of our new high street store. _____

4 Match the expressions a–f to the answers in exercise 3.

☐ a do you feel like going …
☐ b how about coming here …
☐ c it gives us great pleasure to invite you …
☐ d will you be able to come to …
☐ e would be delighted if you could join them …
☐ f would you like to …

5 Complete four short emails. Choose language that is appropriately formal or informal.

1 to a close friend – you want to do something together this evening

> File   Edit   View   Favourites   Tools   Help   Links ➤
>
> Jo
> Are you doing anything this evening?

2 to a group of friends telling them some good news

> File   Edit   View   Favourites   Tools   Help   Links ➤
>
> Hi everyone!
> Sorry for sending a circular email, but I'm incredibly busy at the moment.

3 to a business partner arranging a meeting

> File   Edit   View   Favourites   Tools   Help   Links ➤
>
> Dear Mr Jones
> I am writing to you further to our discussion earlier this week.

4 to a family friend in response to an invitation

> File   Edit   View   Favourites   Tools   Help   Links ➤
>
> Dear Alex
> Many thanks for your email.

4B | WRITING Writing to a friend (2)

READING

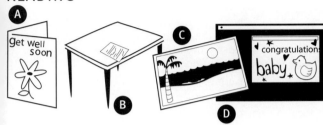

1 Match the messages 1–4 to the pictures A–D.

- ☐ 1 a greetings card ☐ 3 a note
- ☐ 2 a postcard ☐ 4 an e-greeting

2 Match the texts a–d to the messages 1–4 in exercise 1.

☐ a
> : File Edit View Favourites Tools Help Links ➤
>
> Congratulations! He looks absolutely
> gorgeous, just like his dad :)!
> Lots of love from the four of us, Si.

☐ b
> So sorry to hear about the accident.
> I'm glad you're on the mend. Love
> from everybody here, Amanda.

☐ c
> Here we are, on the beach at last. The sun
> and the swimming is really helping my back!
> Hoping to be back on full form next week!
> Say hi to everyone at work,
> Jon

☐ d
> Gone to the
> dentist. See you
> at about 6pm.
> T.

LANGUAGE FOCUS

1 Compare the message to the shorter version in Reading exercise 2. Cross out all the unnecessary words.

> I've gone to my appointment with
> the dentist. It won't take long.
> I'll see you when I get back.
> I should be back at about
> 6 at the latest.
> Love, Tracy.

2 Rewrite these messages, making them as brief as possible.

1
> Sam called to say he's in town. I've gone to
> meet him at the pub. We'll be there until
> about 9pm I imagine. Why don't you come
> and join us when you get home?

2
> : File Edit View Favourites Tools Help Links ➤
>
> Thank you so much for your e-greeting. We're back home now
> from the hospital. It's really nice to be at home with little baby
> Huw. He's a really good baby. He's eating and sleeping well and
> we just can't take our eyes off him!

3
> Thank you very much indeed for your
> kind card. It was nice to know that
> you're all thinking of me! The doctors
> say that things are going very well and
> I should be home by the end of next
> week. Please say hello to everyone at
> the office from me. All the best, Kay.

4
> : File Edit View Favourites Tools Help Links ➤
>
> Thank you for the beautiful postcard. I'm very glad to hear your
> back's getting better. We're all looking forward to seeing you
> back at work again next week, J! We all hope you enjoy the rest
> of your holiday. We'll see you soon, all the best, Rod.

3 Match the replies 1–4 above to the messages a–d in Reading exercise 2.

WRITING

1 Write replies to the following messages. Remember to keep them as brief as possible.

1
> Home at 8. Fancy eating out? R x

2
> : File Edit View Favourites Tools Help Links ➤
>
> Won't be able to make the football tonight. I've done something
> to my knee – again! ☹. May have to go to the doctor's this time!
> Tim

3
> : File Edit View Favourites Tools Help Links ➤
>
> Hi everybody, exciting news: Nina's pregnant!
> The baby's due in September.

4
> Have a great holiday.
> Remember to send a postcard!

5A | WRITING A story (1)

LANGUAGE FOCUS

1 Replace the words in italics with words from the box.

he	him	her	they	them	their

TEENAGE HERO SAVES FAMILY

15-year-old Travis Jude saved housewife Anne Shipley and
(1) *Anne's* three small children aged 2, 5 and 7 from certain
death on Saturday night. It was two o'clock in the morning.
Travis was walking home from the pub when (2) *Travis*
heard someone shouting for help. (3) *Travis* looked up and
saw the Shipley house in flames. Anne was standing at a first
floor window with (4) *Anne's* youngest boy, James, in
(5) *Anne's* arms. Travis didn't think twice. (6) *Travis* ran into
the house and came out carrying the older kids, Suzy (aged
five) and Danny (aged seven). (7) *Suzy and Danny* were
scared, but unhurt. Travis then turned around and went back
into the burning house a second time. Two minutes later
(8) *Travis* came out again, this time Anne and baby James
were with (9) *Travis* and the family were all safely reunited
in (10) *the family's* garden. The fire brigade turned up half
an hour later. It took (11) *the fire brigade* four hours to put
the fire out. (12) *The firemen* explained that the fire was
caused by an electrical fault in the kitchen.

2 Underline the five expressions used to describe the
main characters in the story.

Three students were recovering last night after spending
a night at sea in sub-zero temperatures. The youngsters
had gone out for a short trip along the coast on Sunday
afternoon, wearing only jeans and light jackets. Their boat
ran out of petrol after about half an hour and strong currents
carried the unlucky trio over two miles away from the coast.
The boys' disappearance was reported to the authorities
later that evening when they failed to turn up for a friend's
birthday party. The wind was too strong for **them** to send
out a helicopter that night and **they** had to wait until the
next morning before they could start their search. **They**
finally found the boat at two o'clock in the afternoon,
exactly 24 hours after the three friends had first set out.

3 Choose three expressions from the list a–f that can
replace the words in bold in the story in exercise 2.

a the rescue team
b the boys' friends
c the families of the three boys
d the helicopter crew
e the emergency services
f local newspaper reporters

4 Match each quotation to one of the people a–f
in exercise 3.

1 we were so happy when we heard they'd been found –
the coastguard did a fantastic job
  c the families of the three boys

2 you should always make sure you've got a full tank of
fuel before you set out on a boat trip – no matter how
short _____

3 how did you feel when you realized you were drifting
out to sea? _____

4 when they didn't turn up for the party, we phoned the
coastguard _____

5 when we found them, they were cold and frightened
_____

6 it was hard work flying in those conditions – but it's all
part of the job _____

5 Punctuate the quotations in exercise 4.

1 'We were so happy when we heard they'd been found
the coastguard did a fantastic job,' said the families of
the three boys.

2 _____

3 _____

4 _____

5 _____

6 _____

5B | WRITING A story (2)

READING

1 Match the stories a–c to the titles 1–3.

- ☐ 1 Running late
- ☐ 2 A guilty note
- ☐ 3 A kind word

a

A man returned from shopping to find his car had been badly dented. As he walked up to the car, he saw a note had been left on his windscreen. Laughing at himself for doubting the honesty of the average person, he pulled the note away and read it.

b

A man was waiting to pay at the supermarket when he noticed an elderly lady staring at him. He asked her if something was wrong. The lady began to cry and explained that he looked like her son, who had died in a car crash. She asked him if he'd mind saying 'goodbye, Mom' to her when she waved to him. Because he felt sorry for her, he agreed to do it.

c

A man was on his way to a date one night when he realized he'd got on the wrong train. This was the express that would only slow down, but not stop, at his station. He didn't want to be late, so when the train arrived at his station, he jumped out.

2 Match the endings 1–3 to the stories a–c in exercise 1.

- ☐ 1 When it was his turn to pay, his bill was enormous. The cashier explained that his mother had said he'd pay for her groceries. The cashier, who had heard him say goodbye to the elderly lady, ignored his protests.
- ☐ 2 It said: 'The people watching me think I'm leaving my name and address, but I'm not.'
- ☐ 3 A conductor grabbed his jacket and pulled him back onto the train the conductor said youre lucky i saw you dont you know this train doesnt stop here

LANGUAGE FOCUS

1 Punctuate the end of the third story (c) in the Reading section.

2 Combine the sentences with the word or words in brackets.

1 A man returned from shopping. He saw his car had been badly dented. (*to find*)
2 He walked up to his car. He saw a note that had been left on his windscreen. (*as*)
3 A man was waiting to pay at the supermarket. He noticed an elderly lady staring at him. (*when*)
4 He felt sorry for her. He agreed to do it. (*because*)
5 He didn't want to be late. When the train arrived at his station, he jumped out. (*so*)
6 The cashier had heard him say goodbye to the elderly lady. She ignored his protests. (*who*)

Check your answers in the reading texts.

WRITING

1 Complete the story with the words in brackets.

An elderly lady had finished her shopping and went back to her car in the car park.

1 (*see   four men   drive away   her car*)

   *She saw four men driving away in her car*_____.

She dropped her bags, drew out a handgun, and screamed, 'I have a gun, and I know how to use it! Get out of the car!'

2 (*four men   get out   run away*)

   _____

The lady put her bags in the back of the car and got into the driver's seat.

3 (*shaken   start car   key not fit*)

   _____

A few minutes later she found her own car parked four or five spaces farther down.

4 (*drive   police station   report story*)

   _____

The policeman laughed when he heard her story. He pointed to the other end of the counter.

5 (*four men   car stolen   lady handgun*)

   _____

6A | WRITING A report (1)

LANGUAGE FOCUS

1 Complete the report extracts A–C and D–F with the words in the boxes.

Beginning a report

> following   follows   provide   purpose
> requested   suitability   view

A The (1) _____ of this report is to (2) _____ information about the recently opened Powys Outdoor Sports Centre with a (3) _____ to adding it to our list of optional excursions.

B The report which (4) _____ examines the (5) _____ of Newtown Industrial Park as a location for our new production unit.

C As (6) _____ at the last management meeting, the (7) _____ report provides further details about the accommodation available at Gold Park.

Closing a report

> suggest   suitable   sum   view   consideration

D Taking everything into (8) _____, the site would not seem to be (9) _____ for our specific business needs.

E My own (10) _____ is that the complex would be a valuable addition to our current brochure.

F To (11) _____ up, I (12) _____ we await developments before including this centre on our social activities programme.

2 Match the extracts A–F to one of the report types, 1, 2 or 3.

1 A report on a new tourist attraction
2 A report on possible new business premises
3 A report on a new hotel complex

3 Put the lines in the correct order.

- ☐ the **neighbouring** towns of Padstow and
- ☐ perfectly **located** at an equal distance from
- ☐ equipped and very comfortable and they
- ☐ **overlooking** the Cornish coastline. It is
- ☐ sunsets over the wide, sandy beach below.
- ☐ all **offer** superb views of the **spectacular**
- ☐ **drive** away. The hotel rooms are well-
- ☐ Newquay, both a short fifteen-minute
- ☐ The Seagull Hotel stands on a hill

4 Replace the words in bold in the text in exercise 3 with words or phrases from the box.

> breathtaking   looking out over   situated
> nearby   car journey   provide

5 Complete the sentences with *although*, *despite* or *however*.

1 _____ the menu at the Seagull Hotel is limited, the food is always freshly cooked and of a very high standard.

2 The hotel has no bar and there are no pubs nearby. _____, both Padstow and Torquay have great night life at the weekend.

3 _____ its size, I have no hesitation in recommending the Seagull Hotel for our annual reunion.

4 _____, if we decide not to stay at the Seagull, I would recommend the Royale, which is bigger and located in the centre of town.

5 It is very friendly and welcoming, _____ being part of a large chain.

6 _____ I prefer the idea of staying at the Seagull, I'm sure a stay at the Royale would be equally successful.

6 Use the report form to give details about a hotel in your town or area.

Accommodation report: *local hotels*

The purpose of this report is to provide basic information about (*name of the hotel*) ....

1 **Location**
   It is situated _____.
2 **The facilities**
   The hotel offers _____.
3 **Recommendation**
   In conclusion, I recommend _____.

6B | WRITING A report (2)

READING

1 Read this report of a meeting held by the Blackwater Dive Club and answer the questions.

1 Why was the meeting called?
2 What decisions were taken at the meeting?

Blackwater Dive Club

Meeting: Cocos Island trip
Wednesday 26ᵗʰ, 8.30

▼ Thanks to everyone for turning up to last night's meeting. I think you'll agree it was very productive. Here is a summary of the decisions taken and the action agreed on.

▼ Harriet opened the meeting by presenting the travel options available. We all agreed that we would stay in San José for two nights before boarding the dive boat. As you know, there is no accommodation on Cocos Island, so we will be staying on the boat until we get back to San José.

▼ After some discussion, we decided that we would charter a boat for five days (four nights) from the 18ᵗʰ to the 22ⁿᵈ. Some members suggested spending more time on the boat and sailing back to San José on the day of our return flight. But in the end we opted for another two-night stay on the way back.

▼ Harriet has agreed to book the boat, Jo has volunteered to find out about hotels and guesthouses in San José and Ken is going to book the flights as he can get us a 20% discount.

▼ The next meeting will be on Wednesday 3ʳᵈ at 8.30 to discuss travel arrangements to and from the airport. Please bring any information you can about cheap transfer options.

2 Read the report again and complete the table.

DECISIONS MADE	ACTION TO BE TAKEN	PERSON RESPONSIBLE
Four nights in San José	(1) _____	Jo
(2) _____	Charter boat	(3) _____
Flights from Heathrow to San José	(4) _____	(5) _____
Travel to/from airport	(6) _____	Everyone!

LANGUAGE FOCUS

1 Underline all the reporting verbs in the report and add the missing letters to the list.

1 a _ _ _ e   4 o _ t
2 d _ _ _ _ e   5 s _ _ _ _ _ t
3 d _ _ _ _ _ s   6 v _ _ _ _ _ _ _ r

2 Complete the text with an appropriate form of the verb on the right.

▼ Harriet presented two options for travel arrangements to the airport. After much (1) _____ and initial (2) _____ it was eventually (3) _____ to hire a minibus to take us to and from the airport and Dave's (4) _____ of asking his cousin to drive the bus was (5) _____ on unanimously. Jo (6) _____ to make sandwiches for the outward journey.	discuss disagree decide suggest agree volunteer

WRITING

1 Use the notes to write a report of the Blackwater Dive Club's first meeting after they got back from their trip.

POINTS RAISED	WHO BY
Great trip – despite airport strike. Agreed	Harriet
Write letter of complaint to local newspaper about strike. Agreed in part	Dave Dave to write it
Thank-you card & present (what?) for the crew of the 'Caribbean Star'.	Jo & Ken
Digital photo album.	Harriet
Copies to be made for all club members, too.	Dave Dave to do
Next meeting: screening of Cocos Island DVD.	Ken

L.A. Movie

The People in This Story

| Lenny Samuel | Gail Lane | Mike Devine | Rik Roma | Costas | Homer Frank | Carla Chapman | Arabella | Annie | Josie |

1 *The Purple Palace*

The woman with platinum blonde hair and green eyes put her little finger in her mouth.

'Hey!' she said. 'For an old guy, you're not bad-looking. She sipped some champagne from her glass. Then she smiled. She smiled, and suddenly her whole face changed. Before, she had looked like a naughty child. Now she was a beautiful woman. She had high cheek-bones below her beautiful green eyes. She had a long, straight nose and a wide mouth. Her shiny blonde hair was cut short. Her eyes were shining as she looked straight at me.

'Yeah!' she went on. 'You really don't look too bad. Do you know something, mister? I could fall for a guy like you.'

What could I say? I'm in my early thirties – well, that's what I tell people. The truth is that I'm nearer forty, and the woman I was looking at couldn't have been a day more than twenty-three. I meet lots of women in my line of work, but I rarely meet anyone as beautiful as this one. And on the few occasions when I have met a real stunner, she certainly hasn't wanted to have anything to do with me.

Still, the woman had a point. I'm not bad-looking – dark hair, brown eyes, good teeth, nice clothes. And I've kept myself in shape. I go to the gym three times a week. It's true that my face shows the marks of my time as an amateur boxer. There are some small scars round my eyes, and my nose isn't quite straight any more – somebody broke it in a fight.

'The only problem,' the woman continued, 'is your job. No one ever got rich by doing your job. And I like expensive things.'

She smiled again. She had another point! I was sure that she spent a lot of money, and I certainly wasn't rich.

I'm a private investigator – that is, a private detective – in Los Angeles, California. My clients are often people who live on the edges of L.A. society. Protection, security, blackmail, corruption, missing persons, small crimes – these are the things I deal with every day. Sometimes, I even have a murder case. The only jobs I don't do are divorce cases and marriage problems.

My life isn't easy, but there is usually enough money each month to pay the rent for my apartment and the rent for my office. But there isn't any place in my life for a woman who looks like a million dollars and dresses as if she *had* a million dollars. And the woman I was looking at now was obviously one of those!

'Still, what the hell,' the blonde said. She put down her glass of champagne and took a step towards me. 'Come on, Charlie, we're alone tonight. Kiss me.'

Charlie? My name's not Charlie. It's Lenny, Lenny Samuel. Some people call me Len. Still, I wasn't going to argue. I stood up and took a step towards the blonde.

'Hey, fell, sit down!' a man's voice shouted.

The blonde smiled. I opened my arms.

'Hey, fella! I told you to sit down!' the man shouted again.

I stared into the blonde's beautiful green eyes. Then I felt a hand on my shoulder.

'Sit down! *Now!*' the voice said.

I turned around. The man standing behind me was taller than me, and heavier. I'm one-metre-ninety tall, and I weigh just over ninety kilos – all muscle! But this guy was bigger than me in every way. And he was angry.

'Sit down, fella!' he shouted. 'I can't see the screen if you stand there!'

I sat down and I looked up at the movie screen again. Now the blonde actress was kissing a man. It was a close-up shot'. The woman was thirty metres away from me and her face was five metres high. Her name was Gail Lane. She was the hottest actress in Hollywood, and this was the closest I had ever got to her!

'I'm sorry, fella,' I said to the man behind me. 'I guess I got carried away.'

I go to the movies a lot, especially when business is bad. And just then, business was very bad indeed. My last case had ended a few weeks before. Someone had stolen a racehorse from a beautiful woman. I'd found the horse, but I hadn't earnt any money. Since then, I'd tidied my office, cleaned my car, gone to the gym a lot, and waited for the phone to ring. It hadn't rung. I didn't have any new clients. So, most days, I went to the movies.

—

The movie ended and the lights came on. I got up and went to the men's washroom. There was a floor-to-ceiling mirror there, and I stood in front of it and looked at myself. It was true – I wasn't bad-looking. I was wearing a black leather jacket, a bright checked shirt and a pair of new black trousers. My brown Timberland boots completed the picture.

I took out my dark glasses and put them on. 'Cool!' I said to the mirror, and I walked out of the movie theatre.

It was just before midnight. I decided that I didn't need the dark glasses. I walked round the corner to the parking lot, and I got into my old grey Chrysler. Then I drove slowly past the bars and clubs, trying to decide what to do. It was too early to go to bed. But it was too late to start calling friends to see if they wanted to go out. I was bored. I wanted something to happen.

I was just passing the Purple Palace, one of L.A.'s most expensive nightclubs, when something did happen. A shiny, white open-top car suddenly pulled out from the sidewalk. I hit the brakes and the Chrysler stopped. But the white car didn't stop. It hit the side of the Chrysler with a loud crash!

I was OK. I got out of the car. The Chrysler was OK too – they don't make cars like that any more. But the white car wasn't OK and neither was its driver! The front of the car was badly smashed, and oil was running out from under the engine. The driver was still sitting at the wheel and there was some blood on his face.

The driver of the white car was wearing a smart suit and he had short, well-cut hair. He looked about twenty-five, but his hair was steel grey.

After a few moments, he opened the car door. He walked towards me with an angry face.

'I'm going to make you pay for this,' he said.

He tried to grab my arm. His breath smelt of whisky. Then he tried to hit me. He tried, but he didn't succeed. I used to be a boxer, and this man was drunk! I leant back, and the blow missed. I was about to knock the man to the ground, when he suddenly closed his eyes and fell over. I hadn't touched him.

I felt a hand on my shoulder.

'That guy's a fool,' a voice said.

I turned around. It was a woman with platinum blonde hair and beautiful green eyes!

'That guy's a fool,' Gail Lane repeated. 'I'm sorry, mister.' I opened my mouth to say something but no words came out. I was standing in the middle of a busy street in downtown L.A., with the hottest actress in Hollywood!

'Say something,' Gail said.

'Hey! Well! Mmm – What do you want me to do?' I managed to say.

'Well, let's start by getting my car off the road,' Gail said.

'Your car?' I asked.

'Yeah,' she replied. 'It's my car. He shouldn't have been driving it. He's had far too much to drink. The parking attendant brought the car round to the front of the club, and Mike took the keys. I argued with him, but he wouldn't let me drive.'

'Mike?' I asked.

'Do you repeat everything someone says?' Gail asked sharply. 'Mike Devine is his name. Have you ever heard of him?'

I had. Mike Devine was the son of Joel Devine, who was a rich and successful movie producer. Mike had never done a day's work in his life. But he was never short of money – his father made sure of that. As a result, Mike Devine had got into lots of trouble. There were always stories about him in the newspapers – stories about gambling debts, accidents, women, things like that. Now, Mike Devine lay in the street next to my Chrysler.

Gail and I pushed the damaged white car to the sidewalk. A crowd of people was standing there, staring at us. Then someone recognized Gail. Suddenly, people started to point at us and talk.

Gail looked at me. She smiled and her face changed, just like it had in the movie. She touched my arm.

'There is something else you can do for me,' she said in a quiet, warm voice. 'I can't stay here. People have seen me. I've got to get home. Will you help me, please?'

'Sure,' I said. 'Let's go.' I was delighted. I was excited! Perhaps Gail would invite me into her apartment. There would be soft lights and soft music. Anything might happen!

She smiled at me again. 'You're a nice guy,' she said.

We walked over to the Chrysler. Mike Devine's eyes were open now. There was blood on his smart suit. When he saw Gail, he stood up and held on to the side of my Chrysler.

'Get into this guy's car before the police come, Mike,' Gail said to the young man.

She pulled Mike Devine by his jacket, opened the back door of the Chrysler, and pushed him in.

'Oh,' I muttered. 'You'd like me to take him home too?'

'He lives at 9002, Hollywood Boulevard,' Gail said sweetly. 'Thank you for your help.'

'It's a pleasure,' I replied. 'Please get in.' I opened the front passenger door. Gail looked puzzled for a moment, then she laughed.

'No, thanks,' she said. 'I'm taking a cab. Thank you again for your help.'

Her lips touched my cheek briefly, and then she was gone. She ran to the sidewalk, where the doorman of the Purple Palace called a cab for her. I watched her go, then I got into the Chrysler. There was a strange noise coming from the back seat. I turned round. Mike Devine was being

'That guy's a fool,' a voice said.
I turned around.

I pushed him into the shower
with his clothes on.

sick. I opened the window and drove away. A few minutes later, Mike Devine was unconscious.

—

9002, Hollywood Boulevard, was a tall new building with windows of black glass. I stopped outside it and switched off the Chrysler's engine. A doorman came out of the building and walked up to the car. He was a short, heavy man with a small moustache.

'Hey, you can't park here, mister,' the doorman said.

I pointed at the unconscious figure lying on the back seat.

'Does he live here?' I asked.

The doorman looked at Mike. Then he opened the back door of the car, and stepped away as the smell reached him.

'Yeah, he lives here,' the doorman replied. 'Apartment 501.'

'Help me to take him up to his apartment,' I said.

Together, the doorman and I carried Mike Devine into the hallway and across to the elevator. The doorman came up with us in the elevator, and waited while I found some keys in Mike Devine's trouser pocket. I unlocked the apartment door.

'OK,' the doorman said. 'Are you a friend of Mr Devine?'

'Well, no,' I replied. 'But I'm a friend of a friend. Why?'

'We're very careful about who comes in and out of this building. But if you're a friend of Mr Devine's friend, then I guess you can go in,' the doorman replied. 'But you'll have to give me your name.'

I gave him one of my business cards.

'Huh! A private eye!' the doorman muttered.

'A private detective,' I replied. 'But can you keep an *eye* on my car?'

'OK,' the doorman replied and got back into the elevator.

I opened the apartment door and pulled Mike Devine into a big living-room. I knew at once that something was wrong. All the lights were on. Clothes and books were lying all over the floor. Paintings hung sideways on the walls.

'Where's the bathroom?' I asked Mike.

He muttered something and pointed to a door. I took him into the bathroom and turned on the shower – full power, ice-cold! Then I pushed him into the shower with his clothes on. He made a noise when the ice-cold water hit his face, but five minutes later, Mike could stand up on his own, with his eyes open. I threw him a towel.

'Get dried. Then put some clean clothes on,' I said. 'I'll wait for you in the living-room.'

I closed the bathroom door and started to look around the apartment more carefully. The living-room was a real mess. The windows were open and the curtains were moving in the gentle wind. There was a corridor on my left. I guessed there were bedrooms behind the doors in the corridor.

I opened the first door quietly. I saw a large bedroom. It was decorated in white – white walls, white carpet, a huge white bed.

I stepped into the room and walked towards the bed. I don't know what I was looking for. Then I heard a noise behind me. Before I could turn round, something hit me on the back of the head. I guess I must have fallen heavily to the floor. But I was unconscious by then.

I could feel hands touching my body. The hands turned me onto my side. Someone started to empty the pockets of my leather jacket. They took out my wallet, my business cards, my gun.

I opened my eyes a little. A face was looking at me. It had short blonde hair and green eyes, and it was smiling at me. I smiled back, but the blonde woman's face didn't change. I closed my eyes and opened them again. She was still smiling at me. I moved my head a little. It hurt!

'Sit up!' a voice said. It wasn't Gail Lane's voice. It was a man who spoke.

I opened my eyes wide and saw that I had been looking at a photograph of Gail. The photograph was on a low white bedside table. Mike Devine was sitting on the edge of the bed. He was wearing a white bathrobe with PALM BEACH RESORT written on it. He was holding my gun. And he was pointing it at my head.

'Now,' Mike Devine said in a quiet, hard voice. 'Who are you? And what are you doing on my bedroom floor?'

I touched the back of my head. It still hurt. I looked at my watch. Two o'clock. I must have been unconscious for over an hour. Mike Devine had obviously woken up after the cold shower I had given him.

'You can see who I am,' I replied. 'You've got my business cards. Look in my wallet and you'll find my detective's licence. Then please give me my things back.'

Mike Devine laughed. The gun was still pointing at my head.

'I'm not that stupid,' he said, and he threw the wallet over to me. 'You open the wallet and show me your licence.'

I picked up the wallet and showed him my detective's licence.

'OK,' Mike Devine went on. 'Now tell me what you're doing here. My apartment has been wrecked, and you're lying on my bedroom floor.'

I told Mike what had happened, and how I had helped him to get home. He looked at me and shook his head.

'No,' he said after a moment. 'I don't remember a thing. And I don't believe you.'

He walked over to a phone by the bed and picked it up.

'Get me security,' he said. There was a pause.

After a few moments he spoke again. 'Security? Hi, this is Mike Devine in 501. I've got an intruder here. Can you come up? No, I'm not in danger. I've got his gun.'

Mike hung up and sat down on the bed.

'You're making a mistake,' I said.

'We'll soon find out,' he replied.

Two minutes later, someone rang the bell of the apartment door and Mike Devine went to open it. A moment later, he came back into the bedroom with another man. It was the doorman with the moustache – the man who had helped me carry Devine in from the car.

'Where's the intruder?' the doorman asked.

Mike Devine pointed at me. The doorman gave a short, loud laugh.

'He's a private eye,' the doorman said. 'He brought you home, and he and I carried you up here.'

Mike Devine looked at me in surprise. He threw my gun back to me.

'I'm sorry, fella,' he said.

'I've got a couple of questions,' I said to the doorman. 'Did you let anyone in here earlier this evening? And did anyone leave after I got here?'

'The answer to both questions is no,' the doorman replied. 'I don't let people into apartments when the owner's out. And no one left. If anyone had gone out through the hallway, I would have seen them.'

Mike Devine thanked the doorman, then turned to me.

'There's one thing, Mr Samuel. I don't seem to have any money on me.

'He's a private eye. He brought you home and he and I carried you up here.'

Could you lend me fifty bucks?'

I smiled. Rich people! They're the ones who've never got any money. I opened my wallet and gave Mike fifty dollars. He walked over to the doorman and gave him the money.

'There's no need to say anything about this to anyone,' Mike said.

The doorman thanked him and left the apartment.

I sat on the bed and thought about what had happened. Who had hit me on the head? Had Mike himself done it? If *he* hadn't hit me, there must have been someone else in the apartment. Certainly, someone had wrecked the living-room. Perhaps that person had hit me on the head when I came into the bedroom. But why?

I asked myself the question, but my head hurt and I felt tired. I couldn't think of an answer.

'Look,' Mike said. 'I'm sorry. It's late. Can I offer you a bed for the night? I don't know who's been here. Whoever hit you on the head must have got out while I was in the bathroom. Perhaps they thought they were hitting *me*.'

'But the doorman said that no one had left the building,' I replied. 'So perhaps they're still here somewhere. Or perhaps they're hiding in another apartment. But they must have a key to your apartment. The first thing to do is to make sure they're not still here.'

Together, we searched every room in Mike Devine's apartment. We found no one.

Suddenly, I had an idea.

'I won't take your offer of a bed for the night,' I said. 'My car's outside. The police will take it away if I leave it in the street any longer.'

'Put the car in the garage,' Mike said. 'There's a garage underneath the apartment building, and the elevator goes straight down to it.'

My idea had been a good one. Mike had told me something that I had already guessed.

'So, someone *could* have left the apartment, then taken the elevator down to the garage and driven away without the doorman seeing them,' I said.

At that moment, the phone rang. Mike Devine answered it.

'Yes,' he said. 'Yes, I see.' Then he hung up. He looked terrible.

'Who was it?' I asked.

'Someone I owe some money to,' he replied. 'He said that *he* wrecked the apartment. He said it was a warning. He said he was sorry he had hit you. He thought you were me! And he said that next time, he wouldn't wreck my apartment – he would wreck *me*!'

So the person who had hit me on the head was trying to frighten Mike Devine. And he had succeeded. Mike was looking very frightened indeed.

'Mr Samuel,' Mike said. 'I think I need some protection. I will pay you to stay here for the rest of the night. Will two hundred bucks be all right?'

'Plus the fifty you borrowed,' I replied with a smile. I left the apartment, and went down to the hallway. I told the doorman I was staying for the rest of the night, then I went out into the street. Quickly, I drove the Chrysler into the underground garage.

—

Ten minutes later, I had turned off the lights in Mike Devine's living-room, and I was sitting in a comfortable chair with my gun beside me. Mike had gone to sleep in his huge white bed.

The hours passed. Nothing happened. There were no intruders. I didn't get any sleep.

The phone rang at six o'clock. I answered it.

'Mr Devine's apartment,' I said.

'Who's that?' a woman's voice asked. I knew that voice. It was Gail Lane.

At that point, Mike Devine picked up a phone in his bedroom and began to speak. I hung up immediately, so I never knew what she said to him.

4 Crazy Ellen's

I knocked on Mike Devine's bedroom door. 'It's Lenny Samuel,' I called through the door. 'I'm leaving now, Mr Devine. There's one of my business cards on the table in the living-room. You can send me the two hundred and fifty dollars later.'

Mike muttered something inside the bedroom. I didn't understand what he said. I left the apartment, got the Chrysler from the garage, and drove home. After a couple of hours' sleep, a hot shower and some clean clothes, I was a new man. I drove downtown to my office building, parked the car, and went into Crazy Ellen's.

Crazy Ellen's is a bar, and a café, and a diner, and a meeting place. It's next to the building where my office is, on West Beaumont Drive. Don't ask me where the name of the bar came from. The owner of Crazy Ellen's isn't a mad woman called Ellen, or even a sane woman called Ellen. The owner is a man – an old Greek called Costas. I've known him for more years than I want to remember. I go to his bar a lot. People know that if I'm not in my office, I'll probably be at Crazy Ellen's.

'Hi, Len!' Costas shouted as I came in. It was shortly after nine o'clock and the place was empty. 'Hey, you look tired. Didn't you sleep?'

'Hi, Costas,' I said taking a seat at the bar. 'I'm OK. Give me some black coffee, some orange juice and a couple of fried eggs, please.'

I ate my breakfast and I chatted to Costas about baseball. Then I went to my office – two rooms on the fourth floor of an old building. On the floor of the waiting room, there was a pile of mail. I stepped over it and went through to my private room. There's not a lot to see – a desk, a couple of chairs, a grey filing cabinet, a window with a broken blind. I blew the dust off my chair and sat down at the desk.

The red light on the answerphone told me that some phone messages were waiting for me. I pressed the PLAY MESSAGES button. There were two messages.

The first message was from a man who didn't give his name. The message was short and simple. 'If you know what's good for you, Samuel, you'll take a holiday,' the voice said. 'Next time, it won't be just a little knock on the head.'

Interesting! This was a warning. And it was connected with Mike Devine in some way. But who was warning me? I didn't recognize the voice, and the caller hadn't left a number for me to phone.

But I knew the second caller as soon as he started to speak. It was a man called Rik. Rik Roma and I were old friends.

'Hi, Len, how are things?' Rik said. 'Listen, I may have a job for you. Can you meet me for lunch today? Give me a call.' And he left a phone number for me to call.

Rik's full name is Ricardo and he is Italian-American. His family came from Sicily in the 1930s. Rik and I worked together in the L.A.P.D. – the Los Angeles Police Department. My family is Hispanic – my full name is Leonardo, though people always call me Len or Lenny. My family came to the US from Puerto Rico. So Rik and I had something we could talk about.

Rik and I left the L.A.P.D. at about the same time. Rik went to work as a security man at a big movie studio in Hollywood. I became a private eye. Rik had done very well over the years. He had been very successful in his work and he was now Head of Security at Magic Movie Productions. He always had new cars, and he lived in a luxury house in the hills, with two swimming pools. Me – well, I've got an old car, a small apartment, and a little wooden cabin in the hills. You can guess how well I've done.

I called Rik and we arranged to meet at Gate Four of the Magic Movie Productions studios at one o'clock. I spent the rest of the morning at the gym in the basement of my office building. Then I had a quick shower and drove across town to the studios.

Rik was standing outside Gate Four. Rik is tall and thin, with a high forehead and short black hair. He has deep brown eyes. When he looks at you, you think he is looking *through* you.

I got out of my car, and Rik put his arm around my shoulder. Then he led me through the gate, showing his security pass to the guard.

'You have to show a pass!' I laughed.

'Sure, Len, the security's real tight here,' Rik replied.

We had lunch in the studio commissary – the movie studios' name for a restaurant – with fifteen nuns, twenty Japanese warriors, fifty English

I ate my breakfast and I chatted to Costas about baseball.

peasants, several princesses and a giant.

'We're making a fantasy movie in Studio Twelve,' Rik explained. 'These are the extras – they walk on and off the set but they don't have speaking parts. The stars and the other actors have their own private dining-rooms. They don't eat at the commissary.'

'So what other movies are being made here at the moment?' I asked. I have always been fascinated by movie-making since I was a child. I was really interested.

Rik laughed. 'We don't make very many movies here at the studios any more. Most of the studio area is used for tourism. We get lots of tourist groups visiting Hollywood. They come in to see the old sets – the sets of movies we made in the past. But now, most of our movies are made on location – often in other countries. For example, many of the best people for special effects are in England, so we often work there. And we shoot scenes all over the world. Sometimes we do part of a movie here and then go on location for the rest of it.'

I was disappointed. I'd been hoping to see a movie being made. I told Rik this.

He smiled. 'I'll see what I can do,' he said. 'I'll try to arrange something after lunch. But before we eat, I want to ask you a question. Are you busy at the moment, or would you like to do a job for us? Something a little unusual?'

I didn't need time to think. 'Yeah,' I said. 'I'm pretty busy, but I guess I could do something for you.'

Rik laughed. 'You always were a bad liar! This is what it's about.'

He took a photograph out of his pocket and passed it over to me.

'Do you recognize her?'

Gail Lane was smiling at me from the photograph.

'Yes,' I replied. 'I spoke to her this morning!'

I gave the photo back to Rik and I listened to him carefully. 'You obviously know who she is,' he began. 'But what do you mean about speaking to her this morning? She's working here at the studios today. She was on the set at seven o'clock.'

'Don't worry about it,' I replied. 'I meant that I dreamt about her. I was speaking to her in my dreams.'

'Yeah – so were a few million other men,' Rik said with a laugh. 'But this is serious, Len. Gail Lane is the hottest actress in Hollywood this year. The studio has invested a lot of money in her. She's a big star in the US already, and she'll soon become a world star. That's why the things that have happened have worried the studio bosses so much.'

'What *has* happened, Rik?' I interrupted. 'Tell me. You're being very mysterious.'

'Well, Len, I'll tell you.' Rik spoke quietly now, although the nuns at the next table certainly weren't listening to us. 'This is very secret. Only one other person knows about it. You must promise not to tell anyone about what I'm going to tell you.'

'If it's secret, why are you talking to me about it?' I asked. 'Why aren't you telling your own studio security staff?'

'Because no one else in Magic Movie Productions must find out about this,' Rik replied. 'Those are the orders of Homer Frank, the studio's chief executive.'

'Gail Lane is working on a movie here at the moment,' Rik went on. 'It's an international thriller, and the budget is huge. We're spending hundreds of millions of dollars on this movie. So that makes Gail very valuable. And someone has been sending death threats.'

'Rik, do you mean that Gail Lane has been getting letters from someone who's threatening to kill her?' I asked.

'Not exactly,' Rik replied with a shake of the head. Then he paused while the waitress came to take our orders. I ordered tuna with a green salad and Rik ordered pasta.

'The threats were sent by e-mail, directly to Homer Frank,' Rik continued. 'Gail doesn't know about them. She hasn't been told. Mr Frank is afraid that she'll get scared.'

'I can understand that!' I said. 'I'd get scared if someone said they were going to kill me. What exactly did these messages say?'

'There were three messages, all sent during the last three days,' Rik answered in a low voice. 'They said, "*Death Behind the Door* will be the death of Gail Lane. Stop the movie or we'll stop her." All the messages were the same.'

I was puzzled. 'Sorry, Rik,' I said. 'I heard the words but I didn't understand them.'

Rik sighed. 'OK. I'll try again. Gail Lane is making a movie for Magic Movie Productions called *Death Behind the Door*. The message says that unless we stop making the movie, Gail will be killed.'

Our food arrived and we stopped talking for a few minutes. The tuna was great – it was juicy, with a lime and sweet pepper sauce. I was thinking hard while I ate it. Rik ate his pasta hungrily. There obviously wasn't anything wrong with that either.

'Rik, you've got to tell Gail about these threats!' I said, as we finished eating. 'She might not want to risk being in this movie. You must give her the choice.'

'We can't afford to stop the movie, Len,' Rik said quietly. 'It's half-finished now. There are hundreds of millions of bucks invested in it. Mr Frank won't stop the movie. But we *are* going to protect Miss Lane. And that's where I want your help.'

'I don't think I'd be a good bodyguard, Rik,' I said quickly. 'Gail Lane is

We ran towards the person on the floor. It was a woman with short blonde hair.

very attractive. I couldn't be near her and do the job properly.'

Rik laughed. 'No, no, Len,' he said. 'Gail already has two bodyguards, very good ones. I want you to join the movie crew, so that you're on the set all the time. I want you to keep an eye on everyone else. Perhaps these threats are just a hoax – a joke from a mad person. But we can't be sure.'

'OK,' I said. 'Five hundred dollars a day, plus expenses.'

'Four hundred,' Rik replied.

'Four-fifty,' I said.

'OK. Four-fifty,' Rik replied with a quick smile.

'But what will I do on the set?' I asked. 'I don't know anything about how movies are made.'

'You're going to be Miss Lane's adviser on detectives and investigations,' Rik said. 'In the movie, she plays a private detective. You can tell her about how detectives work. You can start work tomorrow. And bring your passport with you.'

'My passport?' I asked. 'Why?'

'I said this movie is an international thriller,' Rik answered. 'We've finished the Asian scenes already. Today is the last day of shooting here at the studios. After today, the whole crew moves on to South America. When we've finished there, we'll go on to Europe.'

'What scenes are you shooting today, Rik?' I asked.

'Today's scenes will be shot with some of the stars' stunt-doubles,' Rik said. 'There's lots of fighting in today's scenes. There'll be blood everywhere – not real blood, of course!'

I ordered coffee. Rik wasn't telling me everything, I was sure of that. He was hiding something, but what? Perhaps I'd never know.

'But you said that Gail was working here today too,' I said. 'Can I watch the shooting for a while?'

Rik shook his head. 'Sorry Len. It's a closed set – that means no visitors. Carla Chapman, the director of the movie, insists on that. She says that visitors always upset the actors.'

'But I'm not a visitor,' I said. 'I'm Miss Lane's adviser on being a detective. You said so yourself.'

Rik thought for a minute. 'OK, Len. There's not time to get you a security pass. But I'll get you onto the set using mine.'

We finished our coffee and left the commissary. A group of cowboys was just arriving. We walked over to Studio Nine. There was a big sign outside: DEATH BEHIND THE DOOR – SET CLOSED. Rik spoke to the security guards, who let us both in.

'Follow me,' Rik whispered. 'Be careful. It will be very dark inside. And don't make a noise, or Carla will kill us, and there really will be blood everywhere!'

We walked very quietly through the darkness of the studio. Everywhere, there were boxes and ropes, metal wires and electric cables. In the distance, we could see a bright light. When we got closer, we could see that it was a huge, bright blue screen, like a movie theatre screen. We could see someone hanging down on a rope in front of the screen.

'This is a blue-screen,' Rik whispered. 'Later, these shots will be combined with some shots of a rocky mountainside. When the audience sees the movie in a movie theatre, they'll think that the actor was really climbing a mountain!'

I watched in silence. I was fascinated. The person on the rope was still quite high up in front of the screen, at least fifteen metres from the floor.

Suddenly there was a loud scream, and the actor fell to the studio floor! Lights went on everywhere. We ran towards the person on the floor. It was a woman with short blonde hair.

'It's Gail!' I said to Rik.

6 The Bodyguards

There was a moment of silence on the set. Rik and I stared at the blonde woman on the floor. Then people came running from all directions. Rik took charge.

'Stand back!' Rik shouted. 'Get an ambulance!'

I was quickly pushed to the back of the crowd of actors and technicians who came and stood around the woman. I walked slowly away from them. There was nothing I could do.

'Gail is dead,' I thought. 'She died in front of me, and I'm the man who was going to protect her.'

I felt terrible. I had wanted to protect Gail Lane. I had only met her once, but I had liked her very much, even if I didn't admire her choice of boyfriend.

Sadly, I walked towards some other sets which were not in use that day. After a minute, I came to one which was like the inside of a Japanese home. It looked like a real room, but there was no ceiling and there were only three walls. There were several doors which didn't open – there was nowhere to go. And I had nowhere to go now! Because of Gail's death, my job had finished before it had really started.

I left the Japanese room and walked slowly on, through half-built sets, and across open spaces. Studio Nine was the size of an aircraft hangar, and several Boeing 747s could have been parked inside it.

Ten minutes later, I saw something that I didn't believe! I saw her – Gail! Just for a moment, I saw her bright blonde hair, as a door near the end of the building opened and closed.

I couldn't believe it! Slowly and carefully, I walked towards the door. Soon I realized that I was looking at a row of dressing-rooms – the rooms where actors change their clothes and wait during shooting. Each dressing-room had a door and a window. There was a light on inside one of the rooms, though all the others were dark and empty.

I stepped quietly over to the lighted window and looked in. Gail Lane was sitting at a table with a cup in her hand. Her face was wet and her eyes were shiny. She had been crying.

I didn't have time to think about what I could see. As I looked through the window, someone grabbed my right arm and twisted it behind my back. I turned round and tried to grab my attacker. That was a mistake! My feet were kicked from under me. I fell to the floor and my attacker jumped on top of me. I struggled and tried to get free. But my face was pressed against the floor, and the attacker was still holding my right arm. And now they had their knee on the back of my neck.

I tried to turn over. That didn't work. But my left arm was still free, so I reached behind my back and grabbed hold of a foot. I twisted the foot as hard as I could. There was a scream of pain from my attacker, and I quickly pushed them off my back. Then I dived, grabbing the person from behind. I forced the attacker to stand up with both arms held behind them.

The attacker suddenly started kicking my legs.

'Stand still or I'll really hurt you,' I said.

'Oh yes?' a voice said behind me. It was a woman's voice. Then two fists hit me, low down on my back. The pain was terrible. Next, someone's fingers stabbed at the base of my neck, just above my shoulders. I let go of the person I was holding, and turned as quickly as I could. I turned just in time to receive a kick to the head. I spun around and fell heavily to the floor. Then I knew nothing!

When I woke up, I was still lying on the floor. A woman was sitting on my chest, holding me down. Another woman was sitting on my legs.

'Let me get up,' I said. 'I can explain why I'm here.'

'Josie's just been injured, and you're here looking into Gail's dressing-room window,' the woman on my chest said. She had shiny dark hair and

'Let me introduce you to Annie and Arabella, Miss Lane's bodyguards.'

was wearing a suit. 'And you haven't got a pass,' she went on. 'You'll stay where you are until someone from security comes.'

I lay on the floor for what seemed to be a long time. Then I heard footsteps.

'So you think you've caught him,' a voice said. I knew that voice. It was Rik.

The women got off me.

'There he is,' said the dark-haired woman. 'Take him away!'

I looked up at Rik.

'Sorry, Rik,' I said. 'I got lost. And then,' I pointed at the two women, 'these animals attacked me.'

'Fine,' Rik said. 'Let me introduce you to Annie and Arabella, Miss Lane's bodyguards.' He pointed at the women in turn. 'I told you they were good.'

Annie was the one with dark hair. Arabella had red hair and she was wearing a suit like Annie's.

'And who is he?' Arabella asked angrily.

'His name is Lenny Samuel. He's an adviser for Miss Lane,' Rik replied. 'He's going to advise her on how to behave like a private detective.'

'Oh, really!' Arabella laughed. 'What does he know? We caught him easily enough!'

'Wait!' I interrupted. 'What's happened? Gail Lane can't be in two places at the same time. If Gail is here in her dressing-room, who was that over there on the set?'

'The person who had the accident is called Josie. She's not dead, but she's quite badly injured. She was Gail's stunt-double – someone who did the most dangerous parts of Gail's acting,' Rik explained. 'The rope she was attached to broke. It was a terrible accident.'

'Or a warning,' I said. I stood up slowly. My back and neck hurt. I shook hands with Annie and Arabella. 'I can see that Miss Lane is well protected,' I added.

'Yeah – when she wants to be,' Arabella replied angrily.

'What do you mean?' I asked.

'Sometimes she goes out at night without us,' Annie said. 'We can't protect her then!' She was angry too!

'Perhaps, after this accident, she'll be more careful,' I said.

'I'd like to introduce Mr Samuel to Miss Lane,' Rik said. 'But perhaps this isn't a good time.'

'Gail is very upset about Josie's accident,' Annie said. 'But I'll ask her if she'll meet Mr Samuel for a few minutes. I guess there won't be any more shooting today.'

Annie went into the dressing-room and closed the door behind her. We waited outside in silence. Then the door opened.

'Miss Lane will meet Mr Samuel for a few minutes. She can't talk for long – she doesn't feel well,' Annie said.

I followed Annie into the dressing-room. Gail was sitting at a table, holding a handkerchief. She looked up, and those green eyes were full of worry. She held out her hand.

'I'm pleased to meet you,' she said in a low voice. 'I'm sorry, I'm very upset. Josie was a friend as well as my double.'

'Mr Samuel will be advising you on how private detectives behave,' Rik explained.

Arabella laughed quietly.

Gail looked at me again more closely. I could feel her beautiful eyes staring at me.

'Haven't we met before?' she asked.

I thought for a moment. Arabella and Annie got angry when Gail went out without them – when she went out with Mike Devine, for example.

'No, Miss Lane,' I replied.

Answer key

1A Consuming passions

Leisure interests
1 1 take   2 keen   3 give   4 get   5 got
6 passion   7 obsessed   8 into   9 aficionado
10 crazy

Verb forms review
2 1 's   2 has   3 be   4 is   5 have   6 was
7 did   8 been

3 1 Was I?   2 Has she?   3 Does he?   4 Have you?
5 Had she?   6 Were they?   7 Did it?   8 Are you?

🔘 Dictation
4 🔘 01
1 I'd never really been interested in photography until my dad bought me a camera.
2 I've been collecting postcards as a hobby since I was about eight years old.
3 I can't understand people who get obsessive about their hobbies. Haven't they got anything better to do?
4 I really admire those people who have managed to make their hobby into a job.

1B Unusual pastimes

Negatives & questions
1 1 Scientists have not been studying tornadoes for a long time.
2 They do not understand the formation of tornadoes.
3 Tornadoes do not always have a central column of water (a waterspout).
4 Standing under a bridge will not/won't protect you from a tornado.
5 Tornado Alley is not a closely defined region of the US.
6 Tornadoes are not often found in the US outside Tornado Alley.
7 I'm not planning to join a storm-chasing tour soon.
8 Many people had not/hadn't heard of storm-chasing before the Hollywood movie, *Twister*.

2 1 is   2 isn't   3 don't hear
4 did you get   5 Did you do   6 gave
7 didn't follow/wasn't following   8 was
9 Did you get   10 didn't know   11 didn't find
12 are you working

Saying *no*
3 1 I'm afraid not   2 Not to my knowledge
3 Are you kidding   4 Not especially
5 Not exactly   6 I wish I could

Translation
4 Translate the text into your language. Check with your teacher.

1C Autograph hunters

Time adverbials
1 1 begin   2 while   3 first   4 end   5 afterwards
6 finally

2 1 to begin with, at first   2 in the end, finally
3 after a while, then, afterwards

Vocabulary from the lesson
3 1 c   2 b   3 a   4 c   5 b   6 c   7 b   8 c
4 1 b   2 f   3 e   4 d   5 a   6 c   7 g

Translation
5 Translate the text into your language. Check with your teacher.

1D Collectors

What clauses
1 1 c   2 f   3 b   4 a   5 d   6 e

2 1 What you don't understand *is* he's happy enough as he is.
2 What you need to do *is* find something to occupy your time.
3 What Bob wants *is* a bit of peace and quiet after a hard day at work.
4 What you could do *is* arrange for both of you to go out with friends.
5 What your friends can do *is* suggest some other activities outside the house.
6 What you really need to do *is* stop worrying!

3 1 What I was just telling Bob was that he should take up a hobby.
2 What he really needs is to get out of the house sometimes.
3 What I've suggested is he should give fishing a try.
4 What I mean is, it's very relaxing and it would get him out in the fresh air.
5 What Bob thinks is it would be boring.
6 What he'd prefer to do is stay at home and read a good book.
7 What he says is I'm obsessed with unnecessary hobbies.

Expressions with *thing*
4 1 another   2 about   3 past   4 in   5 good
6 those

🔘 Dictation
5 🔘 02
A: What've you bought them for? You've got hundreds of pairs already.
B: They were a bargain and you know I'm crazy about high heels.
A: What goes through your mind when you're in a shoe shop would keep a psychologist busy for years.
B: Oh come on, it's just one of those things. It's no worse than your obsession with movie memorabilia.

1 Reading

1 1 f   2 b   3 c   4 a   5 e   6 d

2 1 F (Only people who got through preliminary qualifying competitions in their own countries could take part in the championship games in Lucca.)   2 T
3 F (Pure logic and concentration are required to do Sudoku puzzles.)   4 T   5 F (Sudoku was invented in the US.)   6 F (The first country in the world where people got the Sudoku bug was Japan.)   7 T

3 1 e   2 f   3 b   4 d   5 c   6 a

4 1 off   2 up   3 in   4 through   5 out
6 into   7 up

🔊 Read & listen

6 🔊 **03** Refer to Reading 1 *All you need to know about … Sudoku* on page 9.

2A Wildlife

Adjectives (character)

1 1 inquisitive   2 cute   3 obedient   4 tame
5 aggressive   6 ferocious   7 cold-blooded
8 playful

2 1 aggressive   2 ferocious/aggressive
3 cold-blooded   4 inquisitive   5 obedient
6 cute   7 tame   8 playful

Present habits

3 1 are often growing   2 are often attacking
3 will forever issue   4 will constantly ignore
5 are often feeding   6 have come

Translation

4 Translate the text into your language. Check with your teacher.

2B Animal rights

Verb idioms

1 1 interrupting   2 make sense   3 misunderstood
4 explaining   5 accept   6 saying 'no' to

2 1 add up   2 face   3 drawn the line
4 missed the point   5 butted in   6 clear it up

Expressing opinions

3 **A**
1 wrong   2 ask   3 concerned   4 convinced
B
a don't   b think   c honest   d Personally

4 1 c   2 d   3 a   4 b

💿 Dictation

5 💿 **04**
To be honest, I can understand why people don't like them. I mean, they're not exactly docile, are they? But it's absurd to say they'd hurt anybody. A playful little bite on the nose, maybe, but they won't mean any harm. They always know when to draw the line.

2C Companions

Past habits

1 1 I remember that my grandmother used to have a beautiful garden.
2 She would spend hours in her garden in summer, watering the plants and tending the flowers.

3 She didn't use to like us playing near the flower beds.
4 So she built a special playground where we would spend hours and hours every holiday.
5 We used to love that playground and I was really sorry when she moved into a smaller house.
6 She still had a garden, but it wasn't so big and on our weekly visits we would play inside the house instead.

2 3 had   5 grew   6 was   10 lived

Strong reactions

3 1 went   2 drives   3 go   4 about/on
5 like   6 must

4 1 blows   2 up   3 lose   4 head   5 livid
6 round   7 totally

💿 Dictation

5 💿 **05**
A: You shouldn't complain. It used to be far worse in his father's days.
B: Was he completely round the bend, too?
A: Totally insane. He used to have conversations with a turkey.
B: But I don't suppose the turkey would make as much mess as the 98 cats?
A: No, but it would make a lot more noise.

2D Working animals

Be/get used to

1 1 get   2 I'm   3 got   4 are   5 is   6 get

2 1 get used to   2 used to   3 used to   4 are used to
5 used to   6 get used to   7 used to   8 are used to
9 are (not) used to

Collocations with *get*

3 1 I first got involved with voluntary work when I was at university.
2 To start with, I didn't really get along with our new neighbours.
3 Stop wasting time and just get on with it!
4 Getting around by car in the centre of town can be quite stressful with all the traffic jams.
5 I'll get in touch with you as soon as I hear any news.

4 *Sample answer:*
You think you have problems? I have problems! This morning I had a big breakfast and arrived at work a little late. I had an argument with the boss, and then was fired. When I came back home, I received a call from my wife, who said it was time we divorced. So I contacted my lawyer, who told me he had an urgent appointment, but I had the impression he was lying. Just as I thought things had become as bad as they possibly could, I …

5 *Students' own answers*

Translation

6 Translate the sentences into your language. Check with your teacher.

2 Reading

1 'compost' – all the other words are connected to birds

2 1, 2 stupid/foolish 3, 4 a stupid, foolish person

3 1 C 2 C 3 B 4 D 5 A

4 1 e 2 b 3 a 4 d 5 c

5 1 rolls 2 hatch 3 burying 4 ignore 5 seals

6 *Student's own answers*

🔘 Read & listen
7 🔘 **06** Refer to Reading 2 *Bird Brains* on page 15.

3A Fashion statements

Compound adjectives
1 1 aged 2 going 3 shaven 4 hand
5 out 6 off

2 anti-establishment knee-length middle-class
never-ending old-fashioned short-lived

3 1 anti-establishment 2 knee-length 3 never-ending
4 short-lived 5 old-fashioned 6 middle-class

Vocabulary from the lesson
4 1 velvet 2 wide-collared 3 Ethnic 4 flared
5 patterns 6 Ripped 7 provocative 8 safety pins
9 make-up

Translation
5 Translate the text into your language. Check with
your teacher.

3B The right look

Expressions with *look*
1 1 got 2 best 3 through 4 exchanged
5 sophisticated 6 have 7 feminine

2 1 d 2 a 3 f 4 b 5 e 6 c

3 1 look 2, 2 2 look 2, 3 3 look 2, 1
4 look 1, 2 5 look 1, 2 6 look 1, 1

Defining & non-defining relative clauses
4 1 who/that 2 which 3 which/that
4 which/that 5 who/that 6 which/that

5 2, 3, 5

🔘 Dictation
6 🔘 **07**
1 Deciding what shoes to wear is probably the most
important fashion decision you need to make.
2 The style, brand and condition of your shoes say
much more about you than all the rest of your clothes
put together.
3 If your shoes look old and scruffy, no matter how
smart your clothes, you will look scruffy, too.
4 On the other hand, if your shoes are expensive and
stylish, then people will think the same of you.

3C Mirror images

Participle clauses
1 1 that/which depicts a young woman
2 that were held to be universal
3 she is dressed or undressed
4 which are now considered unattractive
5 who are starving themselves to death
6 where they are either posing for photographers or
starring in the Hollywood blockbusters of the time

2 1 living and working in modern cities
2 growing up in today's consumer society
3 paid to represent beauty products
4 claiming to cover serious news stories
5 seen by millions of cinema-goers all over the world
6 made available on the internet

Vocabulary from the lesson
3 1 susceptible 2 cloud 3 blemish 4 spotlight
5 set 6 eating

4 1 abnormal 2 incomprehensible 3 pimple
4 puberty 5 self-doubt 6 stunning

🔘 Dictation
5 🔘 **08**
We should have the choice to do whatever we want
with our faces and bodies without being punished by an
ideology that is using attitudes, economic pressure, and
even legal judgments regarding women's appearance to
undermine us psychologically and politically.

3D Model behaviour

Slang
1 1 nuts 2 dumb 3 beat 4 a drag 5 a grand
6 psyched up 7 an airhead 8 blow

2 1 beat 2 blow 3 psyched up 4 a drag
5 airhead 6 dumb 7 nuts 8 grand

Addition
3 6, 3, 5, 1, 4, 2

Translation
4 Translate the extract from a magazine index into your
language. Check with your teacher.

3 Reading

2 1 d 2 b 3 c 4 e 5 a

3 1 c 2 a 3 b 4 b 5 b

4 1 get in touch 2 an audition 3 in character
4 wig 5 facial expressions/mannerisms
6 mannerisms/facial expressions 7 double up
8 competitive

🔘 Read & listen
5 🔘 **09** Refer to Reading 3 *How to be a ... celebrity
lookalike* on page 21.

4A Living in fear

Word building

1 1 distressing   2 fearful/fearless
3 harmful/harmless   4 painful/painless
5 reasonable   6 relaxing   7 risky   8 successful

2 1 fearless   2 unreasonable   3 anxieties
4 cautious   5 painful   6 possibility

Explaining reasons
(so that, in order to, in case, otherwise)

3 1 e   2 a   3 h   4 d   5 c   6 g   7 f   8 b

4 *Sample answers:*
1 He's wearing a mask. Otherwise, it would
be dangerous.
2 He's wearing a mask in order to protect himself.
3 He's wearing a mask so that he doesn't breathe the virus.
4 He's wearing a mask in case there is something
dangerous in the air.

🔵 Dictation

5 🔵 **10**
1 There's no harm in trying.
2 Why can't you be reasonable for once?
3 Put it down. Otherwise, you'll get hurt.
4 I'll say that again in case anyone didn't hear.
5 In order not to make this painful, I'll be quick.
6 I'll spell it out very carefully so that you can't
get it wrong.

4B Bullying

Present perfect & past simple

1 1 *no change*   2 have experienced   3 have also grown
4 have recently started   5 *no change*   6 *no change*
7 has acted   8 have recorded   9 hasn't been

2 1 Have you seen   2 haven't seen   3 did she post
4 've just read   5 Did you know   6 had
7 started   8 ignored   9 got   10 Has she done
11 found   12 tried   13 changed   14 has decided

Vocabulary from the lesson

3 1 assertive   2 bossy   3 confident   4 domineering
5 reserved   6 self-assured   7 timid

Translation

4 Translate the text into your language. Check with
your teacher.

4C The land of the brave

Word class

1 **Nouns:** abolition, disobedience, freedom, liberation,
liberty, move, movement, rebellion, religion
Verbs: abolish, disobey, free, liberate, move
Adjectives: disobedient, free, rebellious, religious

2 **February 11 1990** South Africa's first black president,
Nelson Mandela, tastes <u>liberty</u> for the first time in 27
years.

May 6 1862 Henry David Thoreau, American author of
the essay 'Civil Disobedience', dies of tuberculosis.
May 12 1916 James Connolly, leader of the failed
<u>rebellion</u> against the British, is executed in a Dublin
gaol.
October 15 1969 Millions of Americans take part in
demonstrations organized by the anti-war movement,
calling for an end to the fighting in Vietnam.
November 1 1998 The European Convention on Human
Rights requires all members of the EU to abolish the
death penalty.
December 10 1948 The United Nations Universal
Declaration of Human Rights declares that all people
have <u>freedom</u> of thought, conscience and <u>religion</u>.

Vocabulary from the lesson

3 1 spark   2 regains   3 boycott   4 overturned
5 Mass   6 backs   7 granted   8 racial

🔵 Dictation

4 🔵 **11**

Montgomery, Alabama, is not only famous for the
bus boycott that shook the city in the 1950s. The state
capital was also the first capital of the pro-slavery
south during the Civil War. More than 50 percent of the
population of over 200,000 are black. Martin Luther
King, winner of the Nobel Peace Prize in 1964, was a
church minister in Montgomery from 1954 to 1960. He
was murdered in 1968.

4D Southern snakes

Present perfect simple & continuous

1 1 been being   6 been agreeing   8 been coming

2 1 have been reading, 've read
2 've saved, 've been saving
3 's been driving, 's driven
4 's had, 's been having
5 have been doing, have done

3 1 has been preparing   2 has done
3 has been following   4 has bought
5 has been looking   6 has spent
7 has studied/has been studying
8 has practised/has been practising   9 has left

Translation

4 Translate the text into your language. Check with
your teacher.

4 Reading

1 1 a   2 f   3 e   4 b   5 c   6 d

2 1 D   2 A   3 C   4 D   5 C   6 B   7 D   8 A
9 A

3 1 coming down, descent, landing
2 connecting, fitted to, linked to
3 device, flying machine, invention

4 *Students' own answers*

Read & listen

5 🔊 **12** Refer to Reading 4 *Flying lessons* on page 27.

5A Modern art

Narrative tenses

1 Staff at FBI Headquarters in Washington DC had never given much thought to art. But, with the realization that the country was ~~been~~ losing as much as $2 billion each year, the FBI ~~did~~ set up the Art Crime Team in 2004. Twelve special agents ~~were~~ joined the team after they had ~~been~~ received special training in art crime. The agents ~~had~~ began to track down a long list of missing art works. By the end of their first year of operations, they had ~~being~~ recovered items worth over $50 million. These ~~were~~ included a self-portrait by Rembrandt which ~~did~~ had been stolen from the National Museum in Stockholm.

2 1 was living   2 was   3 had had   4 were growing
5 was   6 had spent   7 had already died
8 was beginning   9 lived

3 artist, collection, dealer, exhibition, landscape, patron, sculpture, mural, figurative, still life, portrait, gallery, painter

4 1 artist   2 collection   3 sculpture   4 mural
5 portrait   6 gallery   7 still life

💿 Dictation

5 💿 **13**
In Stockholm earlier today, it was announced that three thieves had walked into the National Museum and stolen three masterpieces, including a self-portrait by Rembrandt. A police spokesman said that the paintings had probably left the country already. He said that they were working on the theory that the paintings had been stolen to order.

5B Priceless!

-ever words

1 *Sample answers:*
1 he was   2 you do   3 happens/you do/you say
4 you do/you say   5 did that   6 you are

2 1 However   2 Whoever   3 whatever   4 wherever
5 Whenever   6 whatever   7 Wherever

Evaluating

3 1 masterpiece   2 fortune   3 priceless   4 valuable
5 rubbish   6 redeeming   7 worthless   8 worth

Translation

4 Translate the two dialogues in exercise 3 into your language. Check with your teacher.

5C A good read

Past perfect continuous

1 1 Her husband had been trying to get a new job.
2 She had been sleeping at the time.

3 She had been standing in the sun for hours.
4 She had been thinking about it for ages.
5 She had been trying for four years.
6 The crowd had been growing for hours.
7 The children had been eating their dinner in front of the TV.

2 1 c   2 d   3 b   4 a   5 g   6 e   7 f

3 1 had only just turned   2 had been writing
3 had started   4 had been cycling   5 had become
6 had criticized   7 had been working   8 had won
9 had been protesting   10 had been doing

💿 Dictation

4 💿 **14**
There's no question that *The God of Small Things* is a masterpiece. Set in a town in southern India, it tells the story of a woman and her family who have to return to the family home after she gets divorced. The plot is revealed from the children's point of view, with the narrative switching between the present and the past.

5D Bookworm

Phrasal verbs 1

1 1 e   2 d   3 f   4 c   5 a   6 b

2 1 I don't know how she comes up with them.
2 It's not easy living up to it.
3 People really take to them.
4 The publishers turned it down.
5 With the money from her fifth book, she set it up.
6 She moved out of the city to bring them up.

Vocabulary from the lesson

3 1 c   2 a   3 b   4 a   5 a   6 b   7 a

4 1 e   2 b   3 c   4 g   5 a   6 d   7 f

Translation

5 Translate the text into your language. Check with your teacher.

---

5 Reading

1 *Student's own answers*

2 1 b   2 b   3 a   4 a   5 c   6 a

3 1 c   2 a   3 e   4 b   5 d   6 f

4 *Sample answers:*
1 decorate the walls
2 found it hard to survive financially
3 made him famous very quickly
4 spend time thinking about his unhappiness
5 the centre of the action
6 report on/take pictures of the war

🔊 Read & listen

5 🔊 **15** Refer to Reading 5 *Close up: Robert Capa* on page 33.

6A The vote

Real & unreal conditions

1
1 Anyone can become the president of the US provided they want to badly enough and they're ready to work hard to get what they want.
2 Don't enter politics unless you know exactly why you're doing it and what you want out of it.
3 He might have won the election if he hadn't lost his temper and insulted his opponent live on TV.
4 I would only enter politics so long as I could guarantee the privacy of my wife and children.
5 I'll give up my post as governor on condition that I can run for president.
6 He would never have been so successful if it hadn't been for his wife.
7 I would never, ever consider a life in politics, unless, of course, I was asked to.
8 If you want a career in politics, you'll have to be prepared to give up everything else, friends, family and all your free time.

2 Sentences 1, 2, 5 & 8 are real conditions.
Sentences 3, 4, 6 & 7 are unreal conditions.

3
1 If you pick up a starving dog and make him prosperous, he <u>will</u> not bite you. This is the principal difference between a man and a dog. (Mark Twain)
2 If we couldn't laugh, <u>we'd</u> all go insane. (Jimmy Buffet)
3 There is a theory which states that if ever anybody <u>discovers</u> exactly what the Universe is for and why it is here, it will instantly disappear and be replaced by something even more bizarre and unexplicable. (Douglas Adams)
4 Americans will put up with anything provided it <u>doesn't</u> block traffic. (Dan Rather)
5 Nobody <u>will believe</u> in you unless you believe in yourself. (Liberace)
6 Oh, I don't blame Congress. If I <u>had</u> $600 billion at my disposal, I'd be irresponsible, too. (Lichty and Wagner)

🔘 Dictation

4 🔘 **16**
1 If I hadn't seen it with my own eyes, I wouldn't have believed it.
2 I'll believe it when I see it.
3 He'll do anything you ask of him, provided you pay him enough money.
4 I would never, ever consider doing anything like that, unless you paid me.
5 If I'd known, I wouldn't even have spoken to him.

6B Women in politics

I wish & If only

1 1 c   2 b   3 d   4 e   5 f   6 a

2 1 'd known   2 were   3 hadn't done
4 wasn't/weren't raining   5 'd been

Elections

3 1 Members   2 turnout   3 polling   4 constituency
5 ballot   6 candidate   7 general

Vocabulary from the lesson

4 1 involved   2 set   3 run   4 step   5 voted
6 fight   7 represented   8 committed

Translation

5 Translate the poem into your language. Check with your teacher.

6C Politically incorrect

Embarrassment

1 7, 1, 3, 8, 2, 5, 6, 4

Should have

2 1 b   2 a   3 a   4 b   5 b   6 a   7 a   8 b

3 *Sample answers:*
The US shouldn't have fought a war against the Lakota.
The US forces shouldn't have broken the treaty.
Custer shouldn't have been made leader of a cavalry division.
Custer shouldn't have advanced faster than the rest of the army.
Custer shouldn't have ignored his orders.
He should have listened to the advice of his scouts.
He shouldn't have divided his men into three groups.

🔘 Dictation

4 🔘 **17**
I recognize that this government has made a serious mistake and that we should not have taken these steps without consulting the people. I realize that I, personally, should have been better informed earlier and I should certainly have been more honest in the last few months. I can only agree with those people who say that I should have resigned earlier. I was wrong and I apologize.

6D Politically correct

-isms

1 1 a   2 b   3 b   4 b   5 b

2 1 atheist   2 anarchist   3 fatalist   4 materialist
5 individualist   6 capitalist

Asking for & giving clarification

3 1 know   2 suggesting   3 follow   4 mean
5 basically   6 meant   7 point   8 words

Translation

4 Translate the text into your language. Check with your teacher.

6 Reading

2 1 D   2 C   3 A   4 B

3 1 False (The expenses scandal has targeted all three of the main political parties.)   2 True
3 False (It is not known who released the confidential information.)   4 True   5 True   6 False (A former minister has been involved in the scandal.)

4 1 released   2 maintenance   3 tainted   4 audit
5 convicted   6 pleaded

5 1 B   2 C   3 D   4 A

Read & listen

6   **18** Refer to Reading 6 *MPs' expenses scandal* on page 39.

7A Green issues

The environment

1 1 warming   2 gases   3 fumes   4 wind
5 hydro-electric   6 changing   7 food

Vocabulary from the lesson

2 car tyres, chronic illnesses, carrier bags, coastal areas, organic crops, printer ink, plant dyes

3 1 organic crops   2 coastal areas   3 chronic illnesses
4 carrier bags   5 Plant dyes   6 car tyres
7 printer ink

Dictation

4   **19**
Change in the Earth's climate and its adverse effects are a common concern of humankind.
Human activities have been substantially increasing the atmospheric concentrations of greenhouse gases. These increases enhance the natural greenhouse effect, and this will result, on average, in an additional warming of the Earth's surface and atmosphere.

7B Green houses

Futures review

1 1 going to be   2 will rise   3 are meeting
4 will not decrease   5 they're going to have
6 I'll grab

2 1 Are you going to fix   3 is coming   6 I have
8 I've got/I have   10 I'm seeing   11 are you doing

Expressions with *make*

3 1 for   2 with   3 to   4 for   5 of   6 for   7 of
8 to

Translation

4 Translate the text into your language. Check with your teacher.

7C Lifestyle changes

Future perfect & future continuous

1 1 Heather is training to become a life coach. As soon as she's qualified, she'll <u>be</u> looking for work.
2 But before she earns anything, she'll <u>have</u> spent over $1,000 on her training.
3 She'll <u>be</u> having her next class at 3 o'clock on Tuesday afternoon.
4 After that, she'll <u>have</u> done nearly two-thirds of the course.

5 She'll <u>be</u> taking her final exam in December.
6 If she passes that, she'll <u>be</u> starting her 'experience programme' immediately afterwards.
7 She hopes she will <u>have</u> completed all her training by next summer.

2 *Sample answers:*
1 She'll be working on her portfolio this week; she'll be attending a role play workshop at 2.30pm on Tuesday; she'll be having dinner with her classmates on Saturday evening.
2 She'll have finished her portfolio by Friday afternoon; she'll have done two coaching observations by the end of the week; she'll have started work on her fifth assignment before next week.

Vocabulary from the lesson

3 1 c   2 b   3 b   4 a   5 b   6 c   7 a   8 b

Dictation

4   **20**
A: By this time next year, I'll be making millions.
B: You mean you'll be looking for a job.
A: No, I'll have set up my own company.
B: I hope you won't be asking me to help you out.
A: Only once. You'll be lending me the money to start things off.
B: I certainly won't be doing anything of the sort.
A: Yes, you will. And we'll both be laughing all the way to the bank.

7D Trends

Giving examples

1 6, 7, 1, 4, 5, 2, 3

2 If you want to find out about the future, there are many people, ~~among other things~~, who can help you. You can turn, *for example*, to the horoscope pages of ~~such as~~ the newspaper where you can find out about your love life, ~~in particular~~. For more serious information, you can dip into the writing of well-known prophets *such as* Nostradamus or use magical books *like* the I Ching, *to name but a few*. But if you're really serious ~~for instance~~ about the future, you can take a course, ~~in particular~~, in Futures Studies. At the University of Budapest, *for instance*, you can study topics *like* 'Change and Future' or 'Space and Time in Futures Studies', *to name but two*.

Nouns & prepositions

3 1 The developing world's demand   2 The British taste
3 Rapid advances   4 A growing interest
5 An increase   6 Annual consumption
7 A shortage

Translation

4 Translate the quotations into your language. Check with your teacher.

7 Reading

1 1 d   2 b   3 c   4 a   5 e

2 a gossip and celebrity magazine

3 a, c, d, e

4 1 quiet, calm, unassuming
2 one (Alexander McQueen)
3 taking over from McQueen and designing Kate Middleton's wedding dress
4 *Students' own answers*

5 1 intern   2 flamboyance   3 undaunted
4 (wide) array   5 marrying   6 under wraps
7 unassuming

6 *Students' own answers*

🎵 Read & listen

7 🎵 **21** Refer to Reading 7 *Sarah Burton: Dressmaker to the stars* on page 45.

8A Cold comfort

Symptoms

1 1 c   2 e   3 b   4 f   5 d   6 a

2 1 stiff muscles   2 hacking cough   3 upset stomach
4 runny nose   5 high temperature
6 throbbing headache

3 **A:** 3, 1, 2   **B:** 3, 1, 2   **C:** 2, 4, 1, 3

Vocabulary from the lesson

4 1 's off   2 sounded   3 gone off   4 lose   5 take
6 come across

Translation

5 Translate the jokes into your language. Check with your teacher.

8B Bill of health

Health idioms

1 1 She was feeling a bit under the weather.
2 I think I am coming down with something.
3 There's definitely a bug going round.
4 My back was killing me.
5 He was given a clean bill of health.
6 I thought I was at death's door yesterday.

2 1 d   2 f   3 e   4 c   5 a   6 b

Modals of speculation

3 1 Anything ~~must~~ could/might have happened to her.
2 She ~~can~~ could/must/may/might have got lost.
3 She ~~mustn't~~ must have left it at home.
4 That must ~~have been~~ be what she's doing.

4 1 can't have   2 mustn't have   3 might have been
4 couldn't have   5 can't   6 must
7 must have been

5 *Students' own answers*

🎵 Dictation

6 🎵 **22**
1 She mightn't be telling the whole truth.
2 They couldn't have known we'd be here.

3 It can't have been anything to do with him.
4 I can only guess what it must have been like.
5 It may have been her and then again it might not.
6 Some of you might have missed what I was saying earlier.
7 You must have worked out some of the answers by now.

8C Alternative therapies

Modals (permission, obligation & prohibition)

1 1 weren't allowed to   2 had to   3 were allowed to
4 had to   5 can   6 have to   7 don't have to
8 mustn't   9 have to

2 1 have   2 had   3 allowed   4 were   5 don't
6 can   7 aren't   8 must

Vocabulary from the lesson

3 1 low morale   2 growing number   3 full spectrum
4 natural light   5 colour scheme
6 work-related illness   7 ergonomic keyboard

🎵 Dictation

4 🎵 **23**
1 Acupuncture has its roots in traditional Chinese medicine.
2 It involves inserting long, thin needles in the body at very specific points.
3 It is used to treat a wide variety of illnesses and medical conditions.
4 It is particularly popular in the treatment of chronic back pain.
5 It has even been tried with school pupils suffering from stress.

8D Let's dance

Changing the subject

1 1 reminds   2 think   3 talking   4 for   5 way
6 saying

Phrasal verbs with objects

2 1 You should look after yourself a little more.
2 I'll get back to you later today with times and prices for the dance classes.
3 I know I should go and see the doctor, but I keep putting it off.
4 How could you fall for all his stories?
5 You'll never guess who I ran into at the Apollo last night!
6 Don't bring up the subject of his health when you speak to him!
7 When they're late, they usually make up a story about problems with the bus.
8 Can we sort out this problem later?

3 1 They said they'd get ~~me~~ back to *me* with more information about the dates.
2 I've heard enough of your stories and I won't fall *for* them ~~for~~ any more.
3 It's your problem and you must sort ~~out~~ it *out*.
4 It was my birthday, so they took ~~out~~ me out for dinner.
5 Why did you make ~~up~~ it *up*? Why didn't you tell the truth?

Translation

4 Translate the dialogue into your language. Check with your teacher.

8 Reading

1 *Students' own answers*

2 1, 3, 4, 2

3 5, 1, 6, 4, 2, 3

4 1 b   2 a   3 b   4 b   5 a   6 a   7 b

5 *Students' own answers*

💿 Read & listen

6 💿 **24** Refer to Reading 8 *The Unicorn in the Garden* on page 51.

9A Celebrity heroes

Adjective order

1 1 Stylish Italian leather dancing shoes
2 Four exceptional-value original 1960s plastic dining chairs
3 Amazing, life-size, full-colour poster of Natalie Portman
4 Unwanted pair of long, grey boxer shorts
5 Large, black, pointed wizard's hat
6 Beautiful miniature Venetian glass rose
7 Enormous, blue/yellow European flag
8 Brand new super-slim Japanese digital camera

2 1 a huge, black, satin tie
2 a smelly, round, French cheese
3 an old, grey, woollen jumper
4 a long, square, wooden stick

Vocabulary from the lesson

3 1 e   2 c   3 d   4 f   5 g   6 a   7 b

4 1 with   2 of   3 on   4 of   5 into   6 to
7 for   8 of   9 for   10 of   11 as

💿 Dictation

5 💿 **25**
Actor George Clooney has hit back at websites that encourage members of the public to post sightings of celebrities. These celebrity-watching sites are becoming increasingly popular around the world and, according to the Hollywood star, are a threat to the private lives and safety of people in the public eye.

9B Local hero

Adjectives with prepositions

1 1 involved   2 devoted   3 intent   4 restricted
5 connected   6 aware   7 sympathetic   8 familiar

2 1 of   2 to   3 in   4 to   5 from   6 on   7 for

Vocabulary from the lesson

3 1 triumphing   2 inconvenience   3 reveal
4 citizenship   5 sighting   6 update   7 check out
8 psychologist

Translation

4 Translate the text into your language. Check with your teacher.

9C Villains

Adverbs & modifying adjectives

1 1 old, ancient   2 bad, awful   3 big, enormous
4 hot, boiling   5 good, brilliant   6 cold, freezing
7 important, crucial   8 happy, delighted
9 difficult, impossible   10 tired, exhausted
11 interested, fascinated

2 1 pretty, absolutely   2 really, exhausted
3 a bit, quite   4 absolutely, slightly
5 very, different   6 absolutely, totally

Crimes

3 1 mugging   2 armed robbery   3 smuggling
4 vandalism   5 kidnapping   6 hijacking

💿 Dictation

4 💿 **26**
The number one, all-time screen villain who must be on everybody's list is Hannibal Lecter. His cold-blooded intelligence and total lack of respect for human life make him a truly terrifying figure. And it is the relationship between him and a young FBI agent that makes *The Silence of the Lambs* one of the best horror movies ever made.

9D Hate list

Compound nouns (jobs)

1 1 jockey   2 agent   3 fighter   4 courier
5 worker   6 inspector   7 rep   8 warden

2 1 park warden   2 student/union rep
3 disc jockey   4 travel agent   5 health inspector
6 jet fighter   7 drug courier   8 rescue worker

Contrast

3 1, 5, 6, 2, 4, 3

Vocabulary from the lesson

4 1 dazzling   2 thug   3 evil   4 Cynical
5 vindictive   6 obnoxious   7 arrogant

Translation

5 Translate the sentences into your language. Check with your teacher.

9 Reading

1 1 a   2 b   3 b   4 c   5 b   6 c   7 b

2 3

3 a 4   b 2   c 1   d 5   e 3

4 a 5   b 1   c 3   d 3   e 1   f 4   g 4   h 2

5 1 peopled with   2 get their hands on
3 is plagued by   4 flock to   5 took to the streets
6 track down

6 *Students' own answers*

💿 **Read & listen**

7 💿 **27** Refer to Reading 9 *Batman* on page 57.

10A Good deeds

Reflexive verbs

1 1 You should consider yourself   2 Ask yourself
3 adapt yourself to   4 expressed yourself
5 content yourself   6 distinguish yourself

2 It is natural that parents endanger themselves in order to protect their young, both in the human and animal world. But this decision to sacrifice themselves for their children is not always the best choice. How will the children survive without their parents if they are too young to look after themselves? Parents need to remind themselves that they need to look after their own safety first, so that they are then in a better position to look after that of their children. This is also true in day-to-day life. Parents who dedicate themselves not only to their children, but also to their other interests and passions, make better parents. They should not consider themselves to be the slaves of their children, but rather pride themselves on being happy, satisfied individuals who share their love of life with their family.

Vocabulary from the lesson

3 1 from   2 to   3 for   4 to   5 against   6 from

4 1 benefit from   2 attach great importance to
3 sets us apart from   4 gave evidence against
5 sacrifice yourself for   6 provide an answer to

Translation

5 Translate the proverbs into your language. Check with your teacher.

10B Giving

Reporting

1 1 if he wanted her to keep the jacket for him
2 he'd come back for it later that afternoon
3 they were giving it to charity
4 whether they'd be coming back the next day
5 he might be going away for a couple of days
6 when he thought he'd be getting back
7 he'd finished with it and didn't want it anymore

2 1 'Do you want me to keep the jacket for you?'
2 'I'll come back for it later this afternoon.'
3 'We're giving it to charity.'
4 'Will you be coming back tomorrow?'
5 'I might be going away for a couple of days.'
6 'When do you think you'll be getting back?'
7 'I've finished with it and don't want it anymore.'

3 I asked him where ~~was his new jacket~~ *his new jacket was* and why ~~wasn't he~~ *he wasn't* wearing it. He said it had been stolen from his office. I asked him why ~~hadn't he~~ *he hadn't* told me and he said he ~~doesn't want to~~ *didn't want to/hadn't wanted to* upset me. When I told him I ~~had known~~ *knew* the truth, he said ~~was he~~ *he was* really sorry, he hadn't liked the jacket from the start, but he didn't know how to tell me.

4 1 they had found his jacket
2 if he knew about the money in the pocket
3 he had been going to use it to pay a builder
4 her if she had the money with her
5 how much money he had left in the pocket
6 there should have been two thousand pounds in twenty pound notes
7 why he had thrown the jacket away
8 he hadn't thrown it away; it was his ex-girlfriend who had thrown it away

Collocations with *give*

5 1 priority   2 consideration   3 problems   4 speech
5 permission   6 lecture   7 warning
8 piece of my mind

💿 **Dictation**

6 💿 **28**
Can you spare a coin or two, madam? I'm collecting for the poor and the homeless. You may have heard that the hostel for the homeless is going to close down next week, and I was wondering if you might like to give something for people less fortunate than ourselves?

10C Aid worker

Job responsibilities

1 1 promote   2 liaise   3 oversee   4 participate
5 coordinate   6 track   7 seek out   8 facilitate

2 1 participate   2 liaise   3 oversee   4 seek out
5 facilitate   6 promote   7 coordinate   8 track

Reporting verbs & patterns

3 1 They refused to have anything to do with the project.
2 He mentioned visiting our site in the North.
3 She admitted not knowing much about recent developments.
4 They invited us to come and see their new offices.
5 He promised to pass the information on as quickly as possible.
6 They denied having any connection whatsoever with the local authorities.
7 She encouraged me to try again.
8 They warned them not to travel through the mountains after dark.

4 After lengthy talks with our delegates, the local education authority has agreed ~~opening~~ *to open* four new schools in the area. We have managed to persuade them ~~putting~~ *to put* forward 50% of the funding and we have suggested ~~to spend~~ *spending* this money on the school buildings. In return the education authorities have asked us ~~supplying~~ *to supply* the teaching staff and materials.

Dictation

5 🔊 **29**

Working on grassroots development projects requires a great deal of patience and cultural sensitivity. You need to be able to assess the situation from various different points of view and encourage others to do the same. Above all, you must remember that your task is not to dictate changes, but to facilitate growth and development.

10D A good job

Job interviews

1 a to   b in   c for   d with   e as   f to   g at   h in   i to   j on

2 a 2   b 3   c 5   d 4   e 1

Vocabulary from the lesson

3 a meet   b attending   c giving   d set   e write   f develop

Translation

4 Translate the text into your language. Check with your teacher.

10 Reading

1 5, 3, 1, 2, 4

2 1 E   2 B   3 C   4 A   5 D   6 F

3 Topics 2 and 6 are not mentioned.

4 1 defending human rights
2 death sentences are no longer death sentences – they are something less severe
3 people who share your ideas and beliefs
4 making students (on the campus) very aware of the issues
5 does something that will have an effect for a long time
6 doing things together
7 leave money when you die

🔊 Read & listen

5 🔊 **30** Refer to Reading 10 *Amnesty* on pages 62–63.

11A Globe-trotting

Geographical features

1 1 peninsula   2 ocean   3 canal   4 cape   5 falls   6 bay   7 desert   8 strait

2 1 desert   2 falls   3 strait   4 bay   5 canal   6 ocean

The & geographical names

3 The Straits of Magellan are named after the Portuguese explorer who first sailed through this narrow passage connecting the Atlantic and the Pacific. The Straits lead from the border between ~~the~~ Chile and ~~the~~ Argentina in the East, past the town of ~~the~~ Punta Arenas to the islands of the Queen Adelaide Archipelago in the West.

It was the only safe route between the two oceans until 1914 when the Panama Canal was opened, enabling ships to sail right through ~~the~~ Central America. It was a popular route with prospectors trying to reach the coast of ~~the~~ California in the 1849 Gold Rush.

4 1 –   2 the   3 the   4 the   5 –   6 the   7 the

🔊 Dictation

5 🔊 **31**

1 The first people discovered America more than 10,000 years ago.
2 They came from the east, crossing the ice from Siberia to Alaska.
3 They discovered a land which was very similar to Siberia but with no people living there.
4 More people followed and they advanced down the west coast of the continent.
5 Eventually they occupied the whole of North and South America.

11B South is up

Binomials

1 1 short and sweet   2 –   3 bits and pieces   4 black and white   5 –   6 forgive and forget

2 1 Tried, tested   2 Pick, choose   3 To, fro   4 flesh, blood   5 here, now

Vague language

3 It's ~~kind of~~ difficult to say exactly what it is to be Australian. People talk about national identity ~~and stuff like that~~, but it's really much more personal. It's ~~stuff like~~ the things you do every day, your family, your friends ~~and so on~~ and the things you do together. The way we live our lives ~~sort of~~ defines who we are, and I suppose there is a lifestyle which could be called ~~more or less~~ typically Australian. It's a simple lifestyle, an outdoor lifestyle. It doesn't mean we're all sports mad, surfing or kayaking ~~or something~~ all day long, but it does mean that we tend to spend a lot of time outside, ~~you know~~, in our gardens, on the beach, taking it easy.

4 I've loved maps since I was a kid. I suppose they kind <u>of</u> remind me of my dad. He had a huge one in his study. It covered the whole wall. It must have been like 5 metres long <u>or</u> something. We used to spend hours just, you <u>know</u>, looking at the map and planning imaginary journeys and stuff <u>like</u> that. We used to stick flags in it to show where we'd been on holiday and so <u>on</u>. And since I left home I've always, more <u>or</u> less, had a map in my room. And my bookshelves are packed with them, road maps, street maps, atlases, globes and <u>so</u> on. Some people say I'm obsessed and I guess they're sort <u>of</u> right.

Translation

5 Translate the text into your language. Check with your teacher.

11C Positive psychology

Articles

1 1 the   2 –   3 a   4 the   5 the   6 the   7 the   8 the   9 a   10 the   11 –   12 a   13 –   14 –   15 –   16 –   17 the   18 the

2 Researchers believe that happiness, or ~~a~~ 'life satisfaction' occurs most frequently when people lose themselves in ~~the~~ daily activities. The term used to describe this is 'flow'. ~~A~~ People in flow may be doing something very simple, sewing a button on a shirt or cooking a meal. They may be involved in ~~a~~ work, playing a musical instrument, taking part in ~~the~~ sport or losing themselves in a good book. The result is always the same.

The important thing is to identify the activities in your ~~a~~ day-to-day life that absorb you most and to build your life around these things. That, it seems, is the secret of ~~the~~ true happiness.

Vocabulary from the lesson

3 1 Very often other people's ~~opinions~~ *perceptions* of us are much more important than our bank balance.
2 There is no simple, straightforward ~~relationship~~ *correlation* between happiness and money.
3 It is ~~very important~~ *crucial* to take a number of different factors into account.
4 It is also important to remember that we are looking at overall happiness and not single ~~extremely happy~~ *euphoric* moments.
5 But having measured happiness levels, we still need to ~~deal with~~ *tackle* the basic problem of finding ways of making people happier.
6 The ~~really wealthy~~ *affluent* people in society are not necessarily the happiest.

Translation

4 Translate the text into your language. Check with your teacher.

11D Perfect locations

Describing landscape

1 1 estuary   2 hills   3 valleys   4 gorge   5 peaks
6 cliffs

So & such

2 1 such   2 so   3 so   4 so   5 so   6 such

3 1 It's been such a long time since I've seen a really good film.
2 The scenery was so incredibly beautiful that it was almost a distraction from the film.
3 It is such a simple story.
4 But the acting is so good that it really brings the story alive.
5 The closing scene was so sad, it made me cry.
6 It's such an excellent movie and I highly recommend it.

🔊 Dictation

4 🔊 **32**
A: Did you go out last night?
B: No, I was so tired, I stayed at home. I watched *The Lord Of the Rings* on DVD instead.
A: It's such a great movie, isn't it?
B: Yeah, and the scenery is absolutely stunning.
A: So spectacular it makes you want to catch the next plane to New Zealand!
B: Yeah, possibly.

11 Reading

1

PARA	1	2	3	4	5	6
		B	D	C	A	

2 a 2   b 6   c 3   d 1   e 3   f 2   g 5   h 4

3 1 a   2 b   3 a   4 a   5 b   6 b   7 b

4 2, 4 and 6

5 *Students' own answers*

💿 Read & listen

6 🔊 **33** Refer to Reading 11 *Making Slough Happy* on page 69.

12A Loot

Passives review

1 1 was reputedly worn   2 was auctioned   3 was
4 had ever been paid   5 consists   6 is held
7 was once owned   8 was bought

2 1 have been made   2 was first published
3 has been adapted   4 were written
5 were then read   6 has been translated
7 was paid   8 were never used (have never been used
– if you consider that pirates are also a modern day phenomenon)

Vocabulary from the lesson

3 1 raid   2 track down   3 make off with
4 carry out   5 head for   6 threaten

🔊 Dictation

4 🔊 **34**
1 A cruise liner has been attacked by pirates off the Eastern coast of Africa.
2 It is the first time that pirates have attacked a cruise ship in ten years.
3 More than 200 ships have suffered from pirate attacks since the beginning of the year.
4 It has been suggested that all cargo and cruise ships should be accompanied by security boats.

12B Bounty hunter

Idioms (money)

1 Seven years ago Jayne Bingley didn't have a penny to her name. She was living from hand to mouth and struggling to pay the rent at the end of the month. Now she lives in the lap of luxury and has money to burn. It all began when a friend introduced her to eBay. She began with 20 dollars and some bits of old furniture. Now her antiques company is making millions and she's worth a fortune. 'It's a gold mine,' she said. 'I started out in the red and eBay was like a miracle cure. If you've got something to sell, there's always somebody out there who's ready to buy it.'

Passive reporting structures

2 1 are known to have been
2 It has been rumoured that
3 they were reported to have crossed
4 it is now believed that
5 It is thought that
6 who were said to have spoken
7 who were believed to be

3 1 *It is reported that* the Sundance Kid never shot or killed anyone.
2 *It was rumoured that* they were often accompanied by a woman.
3 She went by the name of Etta Place, though *this is believed to have been a false name.*
4 *They were said to be* very polite and gentlemanly.
5 In Argentina, *they were rumoured to be* in trouble with the law.
6 *It has been suggested that* they returned to a life of crime because they were bored.

Translation

4 Translate the text into your language. Check with your teacher.

12c Scam

Phrasal verbs 2

1 5, 4, 2, 6, 8, 1, 3, 7

2 1 turned away   2 fell for   3 hand back
4 ripped (me) off   5 made up   6 give away

Causative

3 1 to do   2 cleaned   3 cooked   4 delivered
5 to come   6 massaged   7 to do   8 brought
9 to decide

Dictation

4 🔊 **35**
1 I'd love to have my whole life turned around.
2 I'd really like to get someone to show me how to manage my time.
3 I've always wanted to have my hair dyed blonde.
4 I wish I could get someone to help me with my accounts.

12D Dollar bill

Generalizing

1 1 People worry more about money than their health, general<u>ly</u> speaking
2 <u>On</u> the whole, pensioners are much better at keeping within their budgets than young people.
3 People carry less cash on them, <u>in</u> general, than they did ten years ago
4 As <u>a</u> rule, supermarket shoppers prefer to pay by credit card than in cash.
5 For <u>the</u> most part, shops and restaurants are happy to accept all major credit cards.
6 People only use cash for minor purchases by <u>and</u> large, such as a cup of coffee, a newspaper or a bus ticket.

US & UK English

2 ACROSS
2 garbage can   5 underground   6 sidewalk
11 aubergine   12 faucet
DOWN
1 petrol station   3 pants   4 vest   5 underpass
7 subway   8 waistcoat   9 check   10 soccer

3 1 garbage can   2 aubergine   3 soccer   4 faucet
5 check   6 pants

Translation

4 Translate the joke into your language. Check with your teacher.

12 Reading

1 *Students' own answers*

2 3

3 1 c   2 a   3 c   4 a   5 b

4 1 e   2 a   3 g   4 d   5 c   6 f   7 b

🔊 Read & listen

5 🔊 **36** Refer to Reading 12 *The Pharoah's Curse* on page 75.

Writing answer key

1A Applying for a job (1)

Language focus

1 1 I translated over 2,000 Recipes from Spanish to English for a web-based recipe book, *La Cocina Española*. The Job involved liaising with my co-writer, Jane Goode, and the Editors responsible for the Project.

2 I am a highly motivated and enthusiastic Graphic Design Student. I am looking for an initial placement in a dynamic work environment.

3 rock-climbing: I was an active member of the outdoor pursuit club at School and have been interested in Rock Climbing ever since.

2 1 Work experience   2 Personal profile   3 Interests

3 1 b   2 a   3 c   4 a   5 c   6 b   7 c
8 a   9 c

4 1 successful   2 experience   3 professional
4 personal   5 voluntary   6 responsibilities
7 essential   8 knowledge   9 referees

5 1 c   2 d   3 b   4 f   5 a   6 e

6 1 chef   2 personal assistant   3 teacher
4 shop assistant   5 film critic   6 museum curator

7 1 was an active member of   2 duties included
3 am experienced in   4 helping other people with
their work   5 at first   6 I am looking for

1B Applying for a job (2)

Reading

1 1 voluntary work with an animal rescue shelter
2 no

2 1 F (Mark is writing in response to an article asking for volunteers.)   2 T   3 T   4 F (He is familiar with the organization.)   5 T   6 F (He has included a copy of his CV with the cover letter.)

Language focus

1 1 c   2 a   3 f   4 h   5 b   6 g   7 d   8 e

2 a 2   b 1   c 8   d 7   e 5   f 6

Writing

1 *Sample answer:*

Dear Sir or Madam,

I'm writing in response to your advertisement in *The Daily News* on January 23 for vacancies on your summer cruises. I am currently working as a part-time receptionist in a tourist complex in the North of Italy. I am interested in the positions you are offering as they would enable me to extend my experience in the holiday industry.

I have worked as a waitress, chef's assistant and receptionist in various hotels and restaurants in the Italian Dolomites and on the Adriatic coast over the last two and a half years, and have enjoyed the work atmosphere as well as the chance to meet new people. I would be very interested in working for your organization, as it would give me an opportunity to widen my horizons, both personally and professionally.

I have included a copy of my CV and the contact details for two referees. I will contact you early next week to discuss the next step in the selection process. Thank you for your time and consideration.

Yours faithfully,

Antonietta Rossi

2A A composition (1)

Language focus

1 3, 2, 1

2 1 b   2 a   3 c

3 1 synonymous with   2 favourite icons
3 the best known of   4 complete without
5 not the only   6 of which less than

4 a 1, 5, 4   b 6, 3, 2

5 1 argued   2 say   3 generally   4 reasonable
5 seems   6 feel   7 agree   8 doubt

6 *Students' own answers*

2B A composition (2)

Reading

1 3, 4, 1, 5, 2

2 4, 5, 2, 1, 3, 6

Language focus

1 1 from a young age   2 At the age of eleven
3 before long   4 From then on   5 Eleven years later
6 at 38 years of age

2 1 brief   2 why   3 famous   4 summary   5 early
6 how   7 grew

Writing

1 *Sample answer:*

Owain Glyndwr is unquestionably Wales's best loved hero. In the early 15th century he led a fifteen-year war against the English Crown and briefly established a Free Wales, for the first and only time in Welsh history.

Glyndwr was born to a noble Welsh family, and, as a young man he studied in London and fought for the English king. But when he married and returned to live in Wales, he found that the country was being tyrannized by English landowners. He led a revolt against a neighbour of his and was surprised by the depth and passion of the support he received from fellow Welshmen. This was the beginning of a rebellion which soon grew into a national guerrilla war.

By the end of 1403 Glyndwr controlled most of Wales. In 1404 he assembled a Parliament and drew up treaties with France and Spain. The war continued to rage until 1409 when the English armies regained control over the country and the rebellion was finally defeated. No one knows what happened to Owain Glyndwr. The new king twice offered Glyndwr a pardon, but apparently he was too proud to accept.

3A A review (1)

Language focus

1 1 in 2 of 3 of 4 by 5 in 6 in

2 1 adaptation 2 story 3 convincing 4 perfection
5 worthy 6 stars

3 1 It tells the story
2 The best moment in the whole movie
3 Most of the action
4 The cast has no stars
5 in the lead role
6 the part
7 which featured
8 Its plot is

4 *Students' own answers*

3B A review (2)

Reading

1 mainly positive

2 4, 1, 6, 2, 5, 3

Language focus

1 1 b 2 c 3 a 4 e 5 d 6 f

2 *Students' own answers*

Writing

1 *Sample answer:*

ER is arguably the most successful drama series on
American TV. The series centres on the emergency
room in a fictitious general hospital in Chicago and
follows the day-to-day lives of the medical staff, both
on and off the ward. It has been running since 1994
and has been the springboard for a host of stars, most
notably George Clooney, who worked on the show for
five consecutive years.
The series is written by award-winning novelist
Michael Crichton, a trained medic, who first wrote
the opening episode more than 20 years before it was
finally broadcast. Although viewers dispute the accuracy
of the medical treatments and procedures, the show is
watched and loved by doctors and non-doctors alike,
and the suspense and drama of the storylines keep it
at the top of the TV ratings, year after year.

4A Writing to a friend (1)

Language focus

1 4, 6, 10, 2, 3, 9, 7, 5, 8, 1

2 1 doing 2 nice 3 quick 4 too 5 again
6 call 7 last 8 now

3 1 Do you fancy going
2 I'm writing to invite you to
3 request the pleasure of your company
4 What about coming round to my place
5 We were wondering if you would like to
6 We would be very pleased if you could join us

4 a 1 b 4 c 6 d 2 e 3 f 5

5 *Sample answers:*

1 Jo, Are you doing anything this evening? We're going
to that new Thai place. Do you fancy coming, too?
2 Hi everyone! Sorry for sending a circular email, but
I'm incredibly busy at the moment. Brad and I are
getting married! We're looking at dates and stuff at the
moment and we'll let you know dates and venues and
things once it's all decided. Love from both of us, Brad
and Jo
3 Dear Mr Jones, I am writing to you further to our
discussion earlier this week. Would you be able to
attend a meeting at 9am next Friday? If not, could you
please suggest a time that would be convenient for
you? Regards, Will Smith
4 Dear Alex, Many thanks for your email. We'd be
delighted to come to the party. It'll be great to catch
up with everybody. Do you know of any good B&Bs
nearby? We fancy making a weekend of it. All the
best, Sue.

4B Writing to a friend (2)

Reading

1 1 A 2 C 3 B 4 D

2 a 4 b 1 c 2 d 3

Language focus

1 I've gone to ~~my appointment with~~ the dentist. ~~It won't take long.~~ I'll see you ~~when I get back. I should be back~~ at about 6 ~~at the latest. Love, Tracy.~~

2 1 Gone to meet Sam at the pub. Will be there until 9.
Come and join us!
2 Thanks for the message. Really nice to be back at
home. Huw is such a good baby, eating and sleeping
really well and we can't take our eyes off him!
3 Thanks for your card. Doctors say things are going
well. Should be home end of next week. Say hello to
everyone at the office. Kay.
4 Thanks for the postcard. Glad your back's getting
better. All looking forward to seeing you at work next
week! Enjoy the rest of your holiday! Rod

3 1 d 2 a 3 b 4 c

Writing

1 *Sample answers:*
1 Can't sorry. Got to work late. C x
2 Bad luck! We'll miss you! Take care, Bob
3 Congratulations! Great news! Best of luck to the three
of you!
4 Having a great time, loads to do and see, will tell you
all about it when I get back. Jen x

5A A story (1)

Language focus

1 1 her 2 he 3 He 4 her 5 her 6 He
7 They 8 he 9 him 10 their 11 them
12 They

2 three students, the youngsters, the unlucky trio,
the boys, the three friends

3 the rescue team, the helicopter crew, the emergency
services

4 1 c 2 e 3 f 4 b 5 a 6 d

5 2 'You should always make sure you've got a full tank of fuel before you set out on a boat trip – no matter how short,' the emergency services warned/said.
3 'How did you feel when you realized you were drifting out to sea?' asked the local newspaper reporters.
4 'When they didn't turn up for the party, we phoned the coastguard,' said the boys' friends.
5 'When we found them, they were cold and frightened,' said the rescue team.
6 'It was hard work flying in those conditions – but it's all part of the job,' explained/said the helicopter crew.

5B A story (2)

Reading
1 1 c 2 a 3 b

2 1 b 2 a 3 c

Language focus
1 A conductor grabbed his jacket and pulled him back onto the train. The conductor said, 'You're lucky I saw you. Don't you know this train doesn't stop here?'

2 1 A man returned from shopping to find his car had been badly dented.
2 As he walked up to his car, he saw a note that had been left on his windscreen.
3 A man was waiting to pay at the supermarket when he noticed an elderly lady staring at him.
4 Because he felt sorry for her, he agreed to do it./ He agreed to do it because he felt sorry for her.
5 He didn't want to be late, so when the train arrived at his station, he jumped out.
6 The cashier, who had heard him say goodbye to the elderly lady, ignored his protests.

Writing
1 *Sample answers:*
2 The four men got out of the car and ran away.
3 Feeling shaken, she tried to start the car, but the key didn't fit.
4 She drove to the police station to report the story.
5 There were the four men who had just reported that their car had been stolen by a lady holding a handgun.

6A A report (1)

Language focus
1 1 purpose 2 provide 3 view 4 follows
5 suitability 6 requested 7 following
8 consideration 9 suitable 10 view 11 sum
12 suggest

2 1 A, F 2 B, D 3 C, E

3 4, 3, 7, 2, 9, 8, 6, 5, 1

4 neighbouring – nearby   located – situated
overlooking – looking out over   offer – provide
spectacular – breathtaking   drive – car journey

5 1 Although 2 However 3 Despite 4 However,
5 despite 6 Although

6 *Sample answer:*
1 It is situated about six miles outside the town in its own extensive gardens.
2 The hotel offers a restaurant, a grill and an extensive bar menu. There is a play area for younger children and bikes for hire to explore the surrounding countryside.
3 In conclusion, I recommend this hotel for short breaks with or without children and as a great base for exploring the surrounding area.

6B A report (2)

Reading
1 1 to organize a diving trip to Cocos Island
2 length of stay in San José, how many days to charter the boat for

2 1 find out about hotels and guesthouses in San José.
2 five days/four nights on the boat
3 Harriet
4 book flights
5 Ken
6 find out about cheap transfer options

Language focus
1 1 agree 2 decide 3 discuss 4 opt 5 suggest
6 volunteer

2 1 discussion 2 disagreement 3 decided
4 suggestion 5 agreed 6 volunteered

Writing
1 *Sample answer:*
Blackwater Dive Club
Meeting: Cocos Island trip
Wednesday 8th 8.30

Harriet opened the meeting by saying that she thought the trip had been a great success, despite the airport strike. Everyone agreed, but Dave suggested that the air controllers' strike had put a bit of a dampener on the trip with the initial ten-hour delay. He continued by suggesting that we should write a letter of complaint to the local newspaper about the strike. There was some discussion and disagreement, with some members seeing the letter as being unnecessary and possibly even damaging to the club. In the end it was agreed that Dave would write the letter in his own name.

Jo and Ken suggested that we write a thank-you letter to the crew of the 'Caribbean Star' and volunteered to write it and bring it to the next meeting for approval. There was some discussion as to what present we could send them with the letter. There were no ideas put forward, but everyone agreed to go away and think about it for the next meeting.

Harriet then projected her photos of the trip on the computer screen and presented a copy for the club records. Dave asked if we could possibly make copies for all the members who went on the trip. Harriet agreed and Dave volunteered to prepare the copies for next week.

The next meeting will be held on Monday next week at 8pm. Ken will be screening his DVD of the trip.